# THE CUBE OF SPACE WORKBOOK

REVISED EDITION

JOY NUR

Copyright © 2022 by Marilyn Joy Nur

ISBN: 979-8-88615-060-5 (Paperback)
979-8-88615-061-2 (E-book)

All rights reserved. No part of this publication may be reproduced, distributed, or transmitted in any form or by any means, including photocopying, recording, or other electronic or mechanical methods, without the prior written permission of the publisher, except in the case brief quotations embodied in critical reviews and other noncommercial uses permitted by copyright law.

The views expressed in this book are solely those of the author and do not necessarily reflect the views of the publisher, and the publisher hereby disclaims any responsibility for them.

Inks and Bindings
888-290-5218
www.inksandbindings.com
orders@inksandbindings.com

# CONTENTS

# FIGURES

# DEDICATION

**This book is dedicated with gratitude to:**

Rev. Margaret Ghazi, who introduced me to Qabalah and Tarot and loved, mentored and encouraged me through years of friendship and study.

Ben Rothell, whose questions inspired the production of this workbook.

Sheikh Din Muhammad Abdullah al-Dayemi, whose mastery deepens my awareness and understanding on a daily basis and whose guidance has enabled me to ground spiritual theory into daily life in a community rich with love and relationships.

# FOREWORD

The Cube of Space is important because it demonstrates the way spirit moves into manifestation, and the way humanity, as the most conscious of God's creation, finds its way back to a fully conscious recognition of God as the essence of oneself. Carl Jung called this journey and the purpose of human life "Consciousness becoming conscious." Within the Tarot we see the archetypal wisdom Jung meditated upon from all of the world's traditions.

We see the cube, manifesting variously as the Kaaba, or cross (a two-dimensional depiction of the cube) appear in numerous mystical and religious traditions because it is a sacred geometric representation of how spirit manifests reality. It also outlines how the material world, awakened as the human being, finds its way back to spirit, consciously. Once we consciously begin to seek our return, we need a map to guide us.

On this spiritual journey, we as human beings can strive for the pinnacle of success if we can understand the nature of our journey and the potential pitfalls along the way. What Joy Nur has created in this workbook for the Cube of Space is an inspiration and tool for any of us who study mystical wisdom.

Clearly, for students familiar with the Kabalistic tradition and its encoding within the symbolism of the Tarot, the Cube of Space is a four-dimensional representation of our multi-dimensional reality.

Unlike a two-dimensional study of the Tree of Life or the spiritual stations of the Yogic Chakra system, this workbook on the Cube of Space shows the more nuanced relationships we can encounter within the process of Enlightenment.

This workbook as a tool for meditation has enriched my own understanding of the universal symbolism of the cube and has inspired me to look even more deeply into the meaning of the Tarot cards as they are placed in relationship within the Cube of Space. These meditations provide a road map through the unconscious and help us to more consciously manifest spirit in our return to the One.

Spiritual wisdom, relationship, personal growth, right livelihood, understanding abundance and the process of taking a project from vision to manifestation are all represented in the Cube of Space as Joy Nur has outlined it for us. We begin as the Fool, full of energy, ready to walk into our unlimited potential, but this road map alerts us to the potential pitfalls and the wise intersections of relationships and potentials we will meet within ourselves upon this road.

The Magician, the High Priestess, the Empress, the Emperor, the Lovers, the Chariot, Death, etc.—as we meet each image and archetypal stage of life within the Cube of Space, we also see the relationships between these archetypes. From each corner and side of the cube, we can better understand the forces that we must navigate, master and meet within and without ourselves upon this journey.

As I have moved through this workbook, I have been surprised at every turn and taken more deeply into the heart of spirit, the emptiness and fullness that is at the center of the cube. At this point, the beginning and ending of our journey, there is the ever-deepening understanding of how life here on earth (represented by the Cube of Space) is a reflection of God's reality. The fully realized person, prophet or sage contains, and has realized the fullness of the potential outlined within these pages. With this ideal ever before me, I continue to enjoy and seek wisdom from this brilliant map outlined by Joy Nur.

I hope you enjoy your journey as much as I am through these pages, and through life.

**Melinda L. Yeomans, Ph.D.**

# PREFACE

The Cube of Space is a diagram of three-dimensional Reality. The Center of the Cube symbolizes the divine creative being that creates and sustains form and consciousness. The outer structure of the Cube then becomes a map of the cycles of life experience that expand our awareness and prepare us to return to our Center wherein we find peace and fulfilment.

The Cube of Space is an ancient Qabalistic diagram that has traditionally been passed down through oral tradition and obscure Hebrew texts. Some of those texts, such as the *Sepher Yetzirah,* have been translated and published in English in recent years. However, their mystical style still makes them difficult to approach without the guidance of a teacher who has both inner and outer experience.

Paul Foster Case had such a teacher, and became one himself. He devised a course of study that made these teachings more accessible by using Tarot as a key to ancient symbolism. His writings are the source material for this book, and his books, particularly *The Tarot: A Key to the Wisdom of the Ages,* are highly recommended as a supplement to this Workbook. He was the founder of Builders of the Adytum, a Western Mystery School that preserves and passes on his teachings to dedicated students. Information about this order and access to his books are available at www.bota.org.

Information about the Cube of Space can be found in his writings and is presented to students of B.O.T.A. within the first year of instruction. But a separate course of instruction on this symbol is never offered and many students have difficulty visualizing a three-dimensional symbol. This workbook is designed for those students. In this book, the Cube of Space is diagrammed from every point of view. A brief suggestion points the student to a way of working with each diagram. Questions then ask the student to correlate the related symbols as a guide to their study and meditation. By working with these symbols, each student will be led to their own insights that are relevant to their lives and spiritual awakening.

Meditation on the Cube of Space offers deep insight on the meaning of Tarot and reveals many ways to understand life experience. The relationship between mental processes and physical experience, the process and progress toward enlightenment, and the nature and purpose of cycles of life experience are profoundly illuminated by the study of the relationships revealed in the Cube of Space. By applying insights from a study of the Cube of Space, a person may achieve a deeper understanding of almost any field of knowledge. One way this happens is that the Cube shows us the usually hidden subconscious activity that informs our outer experience.

This workbook is divided into sections that focus on the Cube of Space from different perspectives. It is not necessary to work your way sequentially through the book to benefit from it. Any section may be studied as a unit. Alternatively, a particular Tarot Key can be studied in depth by examining the figures that feature it in each section.

Please do not take my comments and questions as definitive or authoritative interpretations of the Cube of Space. They are intentionally brief and meant to be suggestions to stimulate your own meditations. Each person brings to this study a unique point of view and background that can result in their own realization and insight.

Cubic symbols are found in many traditional systems. The Holy of Holies in the Temple of Solomon was a cube. The Kaaba, which is at the geographic center of Muslim worship in Mecca, is a cube. The cube opened out becomes a cross. The directions of space carry symbolic meanings in most traditions, including the American Indian traditions.

Many students find that constructing a three-dimensional cube enhances their studies. A clear Plexiglas picture cube can be a basis for a diagram with pictures of Tarot cards glued to its sides and edges. A beautiful Cube can be made from one-foot squares of glass or Plexiglas glued to edges made of painted molding. Inner coordinates can be inserted using thin, flexible dowels and/or colored thread or twine.

May your capacity for love and life keep growing as you study.

L.V.X.—Light in extension.

**Soror Joy**

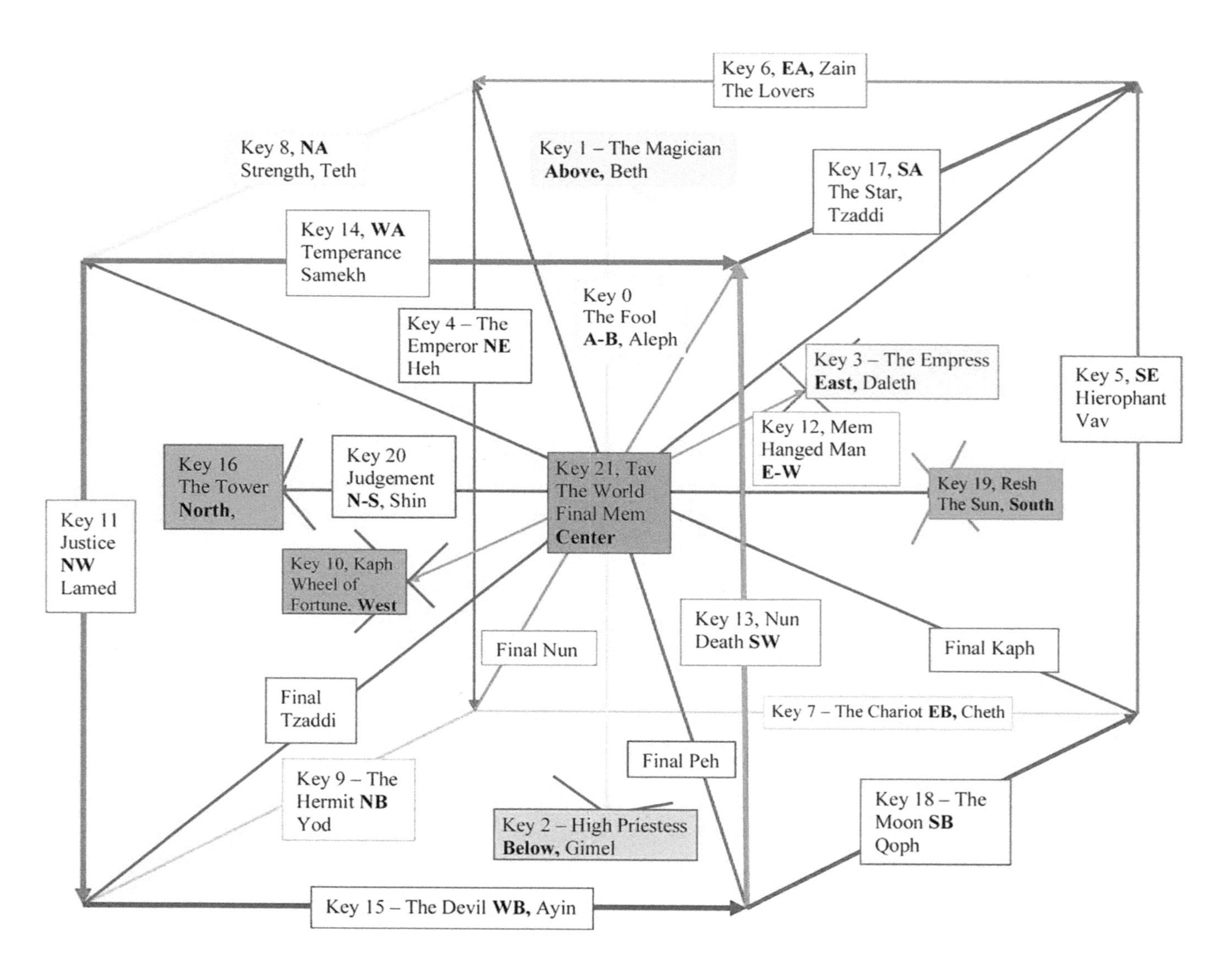


**Fig 0**

Cube of Space with Attributions

# INTRODUCTION

## The Cube of Space as a whole

The Cube of Space is a symbol for the container of creation, Reality in manifestation. The number of the cube is 26 (6 sides, 12 edges, 8 corners). This is the number of YHVH (יהוה) the sacred Hebrew name for God. To travel around the Cube of Space is to complete a cycle of manifestation. To be fully aware is to experience the fullness of the Cube of Space within your life.

Although in this study the Cube will be presented from every point of view, the conventional diagram of the Cube of Space as a whole is from the west face. This correlates with the conventional directions of the Tarot Keys in which the background of most Keys is in the east and the foreground is in the west. However, to see the Cube as a whole, it is necessary to assume a transparent Cube, because a solid cube allows the viewer to see no more than three sides at once. Since the west side of the Cube symbolizes the outer appearances of life and the east side of the Cube the inner processes of creative imagination, putting the west face in front subtly suggests where we begin our process of growth in awareness.

Note that each of the Hebrew letters has a correspondence on the Cube of Space. The "mother letters," Aleph, Mem, and Shin, attributed to the outer planets in astrology, are assigned to the inner coordinates that originate at the center of the Cube and flow outward to the faces of the Cube of Space. The "double letters," Beth, Gimel, Daleth, Kaph, Peh, Resh, and Tav, have two sounds and are attributed to the inner planets. They are assigned to the faces of the Cube of Space and its center. The rest of the letters, the twelve "single letters," attributed to the signs of the zodiac, are assigned to the sides of the Cube of Space where the faces intersect. Four of the five Hebrew final letters, Final Kaph, Nun, Peh, and Tzaddi, are assigned to the diagonals, which begin at the lower corners of the Cube of Space and intersect at the center on their way to the upper corners of the Cube. The fifth final letter, Final Mem, is assigned to the center of the Cube of Space along with the Hebrew letter Tav. These final letters have a different form when they come at the end of a word and are represented on the outside of the Cube in their regular forms.

Also note that each line defining the Cube of Space is given a direction. These are important in examining the meanings of each line and how adjacent Tarot Keys are related to each other on the Cube of Space. The directions of flow are related to the cycles of manifestation and create a sense of dynamic movement within the stability of the cubic form.

Throughout this study, as the Cube of Space is presented from each point of view, try to visualize the Cube in three dimensions and full color. This will be an invaluable aid in learning and remembering the makeup of the Cube of Space. Visualizing yourself within the Cube of Space can also be an excellent way to begin a meditation on the Cube of Space that can make it an experience for the whole self, rather than a simple intellectual exercise.

## Question for contemplation:

What are your impressions as you look at the Cube of Space as a whole?

# THE CUBE OF SPACE AS A WHOLE

## ILLUSTRATED WITH TAROT KEYS

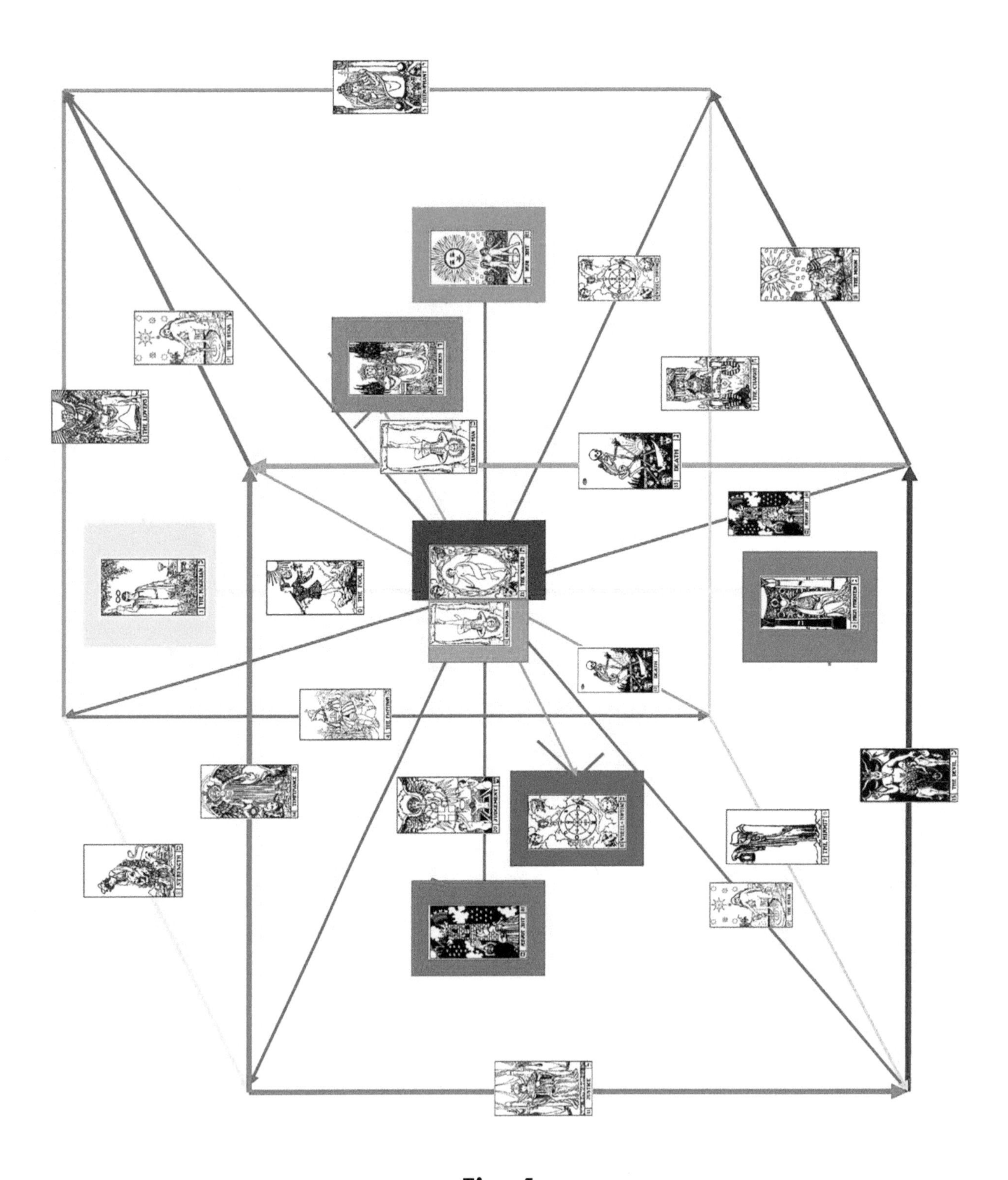

**Fig. 1**

The Inner Coordinates and the Faces—The Planets

## The Structure of the Cube of Space—From the Inside Out

This section of the workbook examines the structure of the Cube of Space. The Cube is created from within. At the center is Key 21 (The World, Tav), attributed to Saturn and Cosmic Consciousness. All potential manifestation expressed in the Cube of Space originates here. Our sense of being centered comes from this point. The path of return also ends here, as the diagonals within the Cube all meet at this point. The diagonals, by which one returns to the center of the Cube of Space, will be examined in depth in the last section of the workbook, because they are attributed to the final forms of the letters. They can be traversed only when outer experience has sufficiently developed the personality.

From the center radiate the inner coordinates corresponding to the three outer planets of astrology and Tarot Keys 0 (The Fool, Uranus), 12 (Hanged Man, Neptune), and 20 (Judgement, Pluto). These correspond to the mother letters of the Hebrew alphabet. All relate to super-consciousness or divine influence and impact us as impulses from the soul and circumstances beyond our personal control.

The energy from these inner coordinates creates the six faces of the Cube of Space, assigned to the inner, personal planets and their corresponding Hebrew double letters. (Double letters have two sounds.) The boundaries of these faces, where they meet, are assigned to the twelve Hebrew single letters and Tarot Keys corresponding to the signs of the zodiac. Since the faces of the Cube of Space will be examined in relation to the Tarot Keys associated with their edges, by the end of this section, all of the Cube of Space will be covered except for the diagonals. An introductory course of lessons on the Cube of Space could include the sections associated with figures 2, 6, 7, 8, 9, 10, 11, and 1 of this work-book. Figure 1 in this series is the most complex and includes the diagonals, so I suggest it as a good way to summarize the series.

This section of the study emphasizes the stages of our journey through life, the different perspectives from which we can interpret our experience, and the resources from which we can draw guidance and energy.

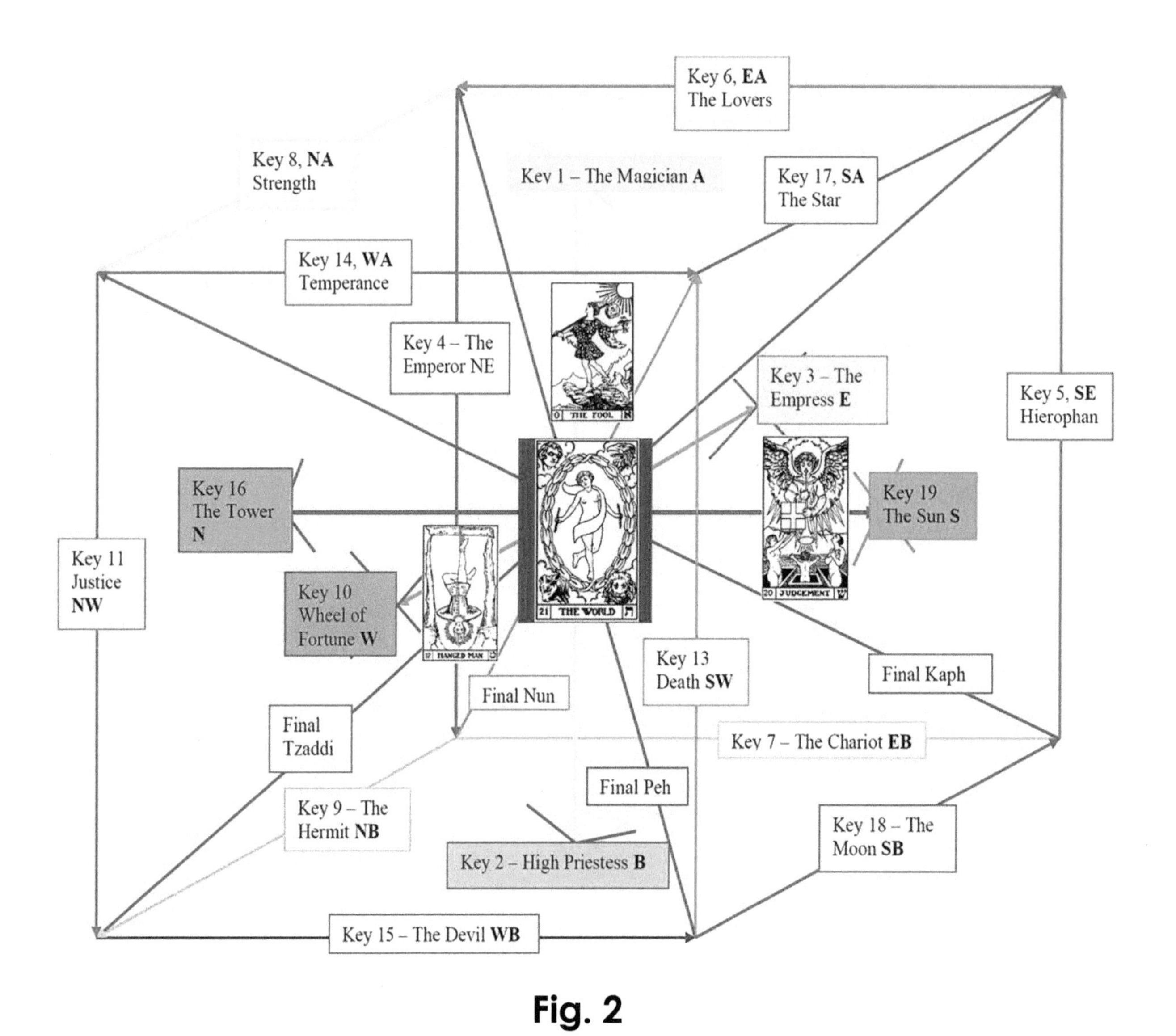


**Fig. 2**

The Center of the Cube: The World—Saturn

## Creation of the Cube of Space from the Center

At the center of the Cube of Space is Tarot Key 21, The World, attributed to Saturn. From the center, rays go to each of the six directions to create the faces of the Cube. The rays going up and down from the center are attributed to Key 0, The Fool. The rays going to the east and the west from the center are attributed to Key 12, Hanged Man. The rays going to the north and the south from the center are attributed to Key 20, Judgement. The potential length of these rays is infinite. The faces of the Cube are always at the end of these rays, being "pushed" by them.

The faces represent the outer structure of the Cube of Space manifesting dual expressions within time and space of the inner creative power of the rays. The inner rays represent a superconscious trinity of expression that underlies the outer structure of The World. The administration of the creative process is at the center of the Cube (Key 21). The entire creative process is omniscient (Key 0), omnipotent (Key 20), and omnipresent (Key 12.) Meditate on this diagram to help you "get centered" and recognize the Reality at the core of all appearances.

### Questions for contemplation:

1. What associations do you have with The World?

2. What correlates with the Hebrew letter Tav?

   A. Aleph
   B. Mem
   C. Shin

3. What powers are associated with the numbers on these Tarot Keys?

   A. 21
   B. 12
   C. 0
   D. 20

4. What are the astrological attributions of these Tarot Keys?

   A. Key 21
   B. Key 0
   C. Key 12
   D. Key 20

5. What are the relationships between Key 21 and Binah (3rd sphere, Understanding) and Malkuth (10th sphere, Kingdom) on the Tree of Life https://www.bota.org/resources/ and what does that suggest about the significance of the Cube?

6. The figure in The World seems to be dancing on air. If she represents the Dance of Life, what aspects of the dance are represented by The Fool?

   A. Hanged Man
   B. Judgement

7. What are the elements and colors associated with these Tarot Keys and what do they suggest?

   A. Key 21
   B. Key 0
   C. Key 12
   D. Key 20

8. How does this point of view of the Cube of Space relate to being centered or grounded?

9. What other observations or feelings are associated with the interior of the Cube of Space?

Reflections:

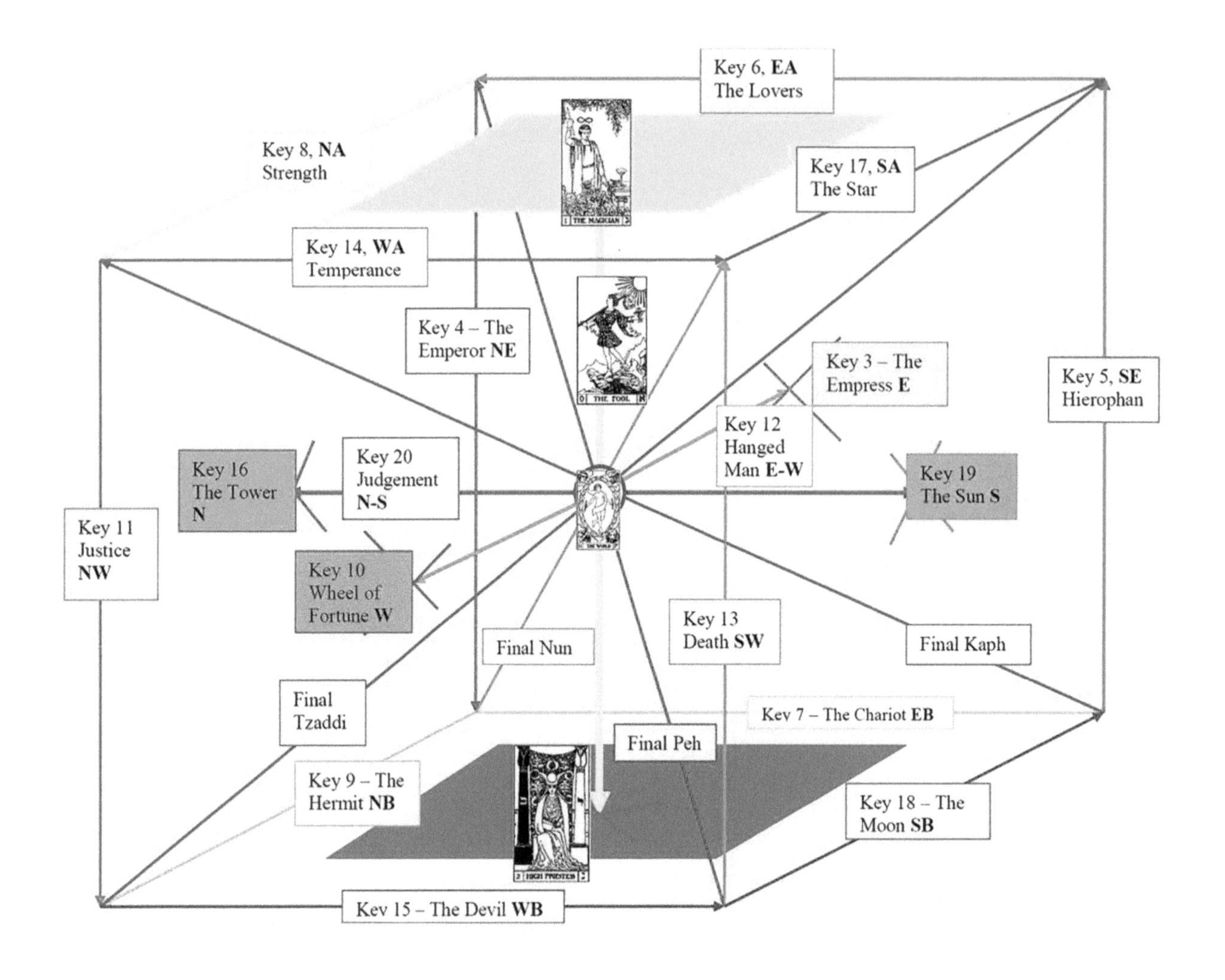


**Fig. 3**

Above-Below Coordinate: The Fool—Uranus

## The Coordinate of Consciousness

From the center of the Cube of Space, the ray attributed to Tarot Key 0 (The Fool, Uranus) flows upward until it meets the top of the Above face of the Cube, attributed to Tarot Key 1 (The Magician, Mercury). Tarot Key 0 is also attributed to the ray that flows from the center downward to the bottom, or the Below face of the Cube, attributed to Tarot Key 2 (High Priestess, Moon). Within our mind is a consciousness totally free from limiting conditions that knows the goal of the creative process (Key 0). Awareness of that freedom can transform our lives (Key 1) and distill the gifts held in our memory (Key 2), separating the developed capacities from the sometimes painful experiences that created them. Meditate on this coordinate to grasp a sense of Divine purpose at the core of the creative process.

### Questions for contemplation:

These Tarot Keys are all associated with different aspects of consciousness.

1. What aspect of consciousness is assigned to Key 0?

   A. Key 1
   B. Key 2

2. What associations can you make with The Fool?

   A. The Magician
   B. High Priestess

3. What correlations can be made with the Hebrew letter Aleph?

   A. Beth
   B. Gimel

4. What are the astrological attributions of these Tarot Keys?

   A. Key 0
   B. Key 1
   C. Key 2

5. What do the positions of the paths attributed to these Tarot Keys on the Tree of Life suggest about the Cube of Space?

6. What is the significance of the relationship of these Tarot Keys to the Center of the Cube of Space and to Key 21 (The World, Saturn)?

7. What meaning do the colors of these Tarot Keys have for you?

8. What associations do you have with the directions up and down?

9. What type of awareness does this view of the Cube awaken?

10. What is the relationship between this path and our willingness and capacity to experiment to gain more understanding?

11. What is the relationship between this path and the element of air?

Reflections:

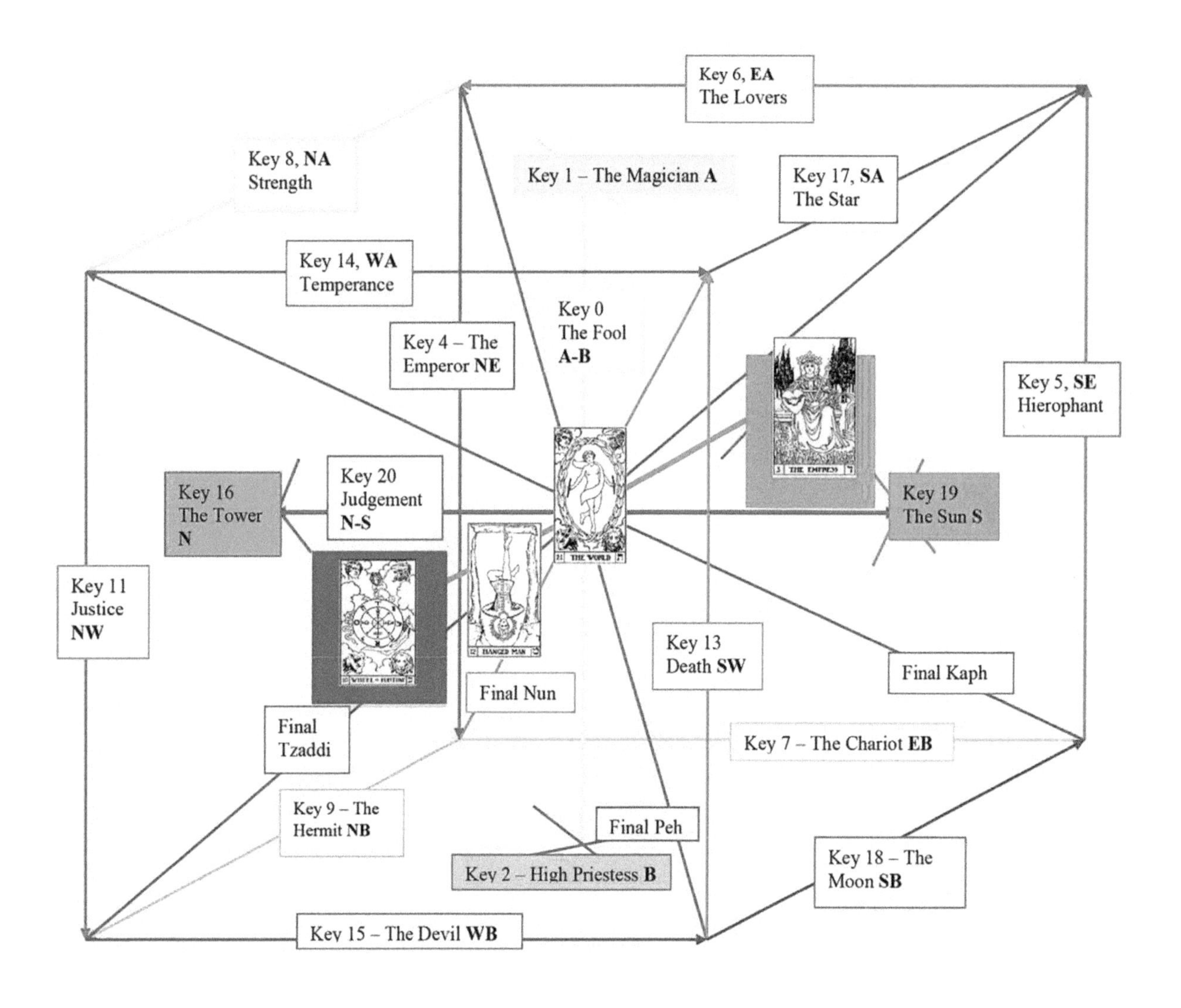


**Fig. 4**

East-West Coordinate: Hanged Man—Neptune

## The Coordinate of Substance

From the center of the Cube of Space, the ray attributed to Tarot Key 12 (Hanged Man, Neptune) flows to the east, meeting the face of the Cube attributed to Tarot Key 3 (The Empress, Venus) and to the west, meeting the face attributed to Tarot Key 10 (Wheel of Fortune, Jupiter). Since East represents creative activity and West represents creation in form, this coordinate relates to the inner aspects of the creative work of manifestation. The flow of divine substance (Key 12) takes form in the creative images (Key 3) that affect the cycles of manifestation (Key 10). Meditate on this coordinate to deepen your awareness of the infinite source of supply for all your needs

### Questions for contemplation:

The Tarot Keys related to this coordinate all have a relationship to mental substance.

1. What form does that take in Tarot Key 12?

   A. Key 3
   B. Key 10
   C. Key 21

2. What associations do you have with Hanged Man?

   A. The Empress
   B. Wheel of Fortune

3. What correlations can you find with the Hebrew letter Mem?
   A. Daleth
   B. Kaph

4. What are the astrological correlations with Tarot Key 12?

   A. Key 3
   B. Key 10

5. How does will or intention relate to this coordinate and to each of these Tarot Keys?

   A. Key 21
   B. Key 12
   C. Key 3
   D. Key 10

6. How do these Tarot Keys relate to creative expression?

   A. Key 12
   B. Key 3
   C. Key 10

7. How do these Tarot Keys relate to the cycles of life?

8. How does this view of the Cube of Space relate to surrender?

9. How does the element of water and the quality of memory work in these Tarot Keys?

A. Key 21
B. Key 12
C. Key 3
D. Key 10

Reflections:

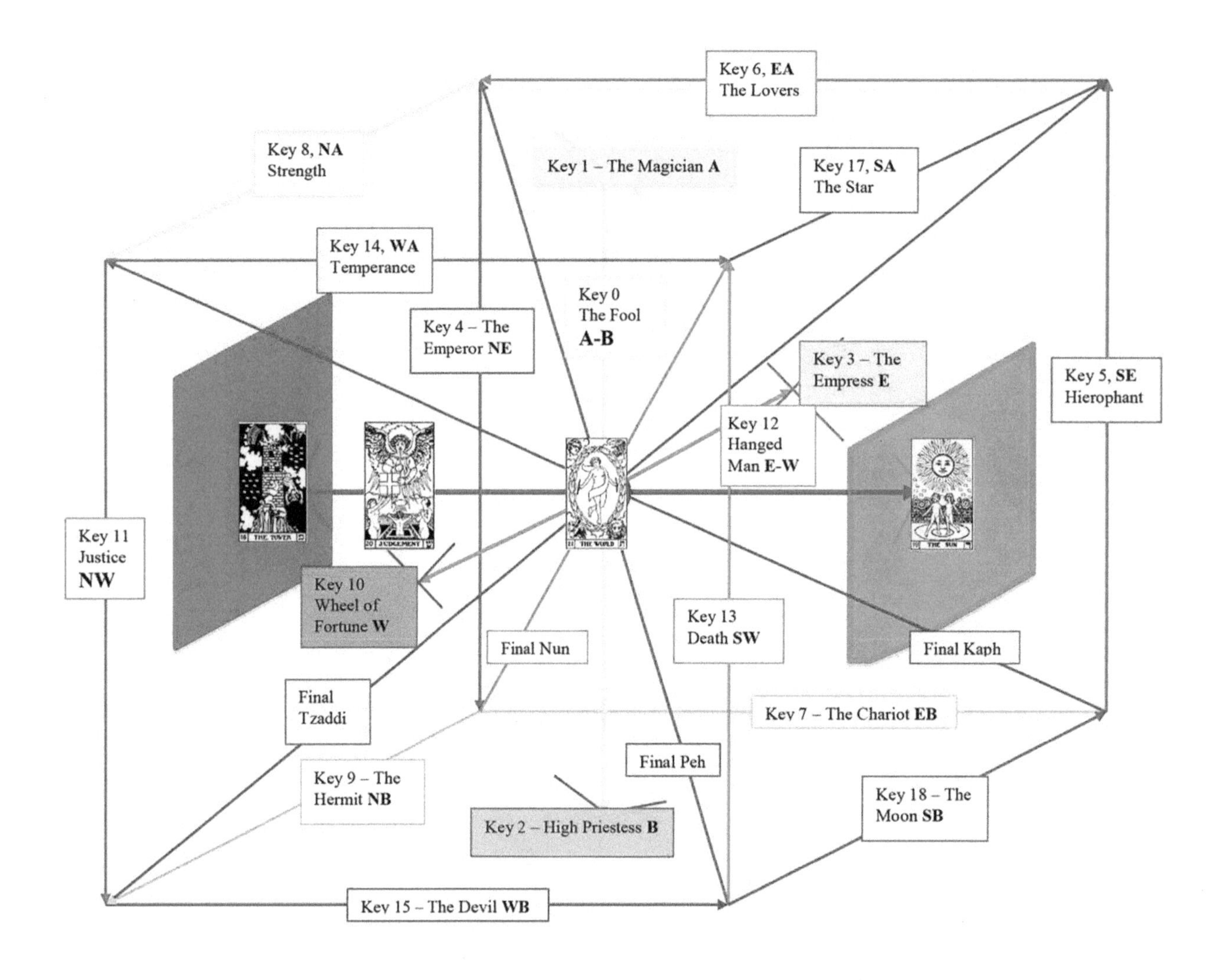


**Fig. 5**

North-South Coordinate: Judgement—Pluto

## The Coordinate of Activity

From the center of the Cube of Space, the ray attributed to Tarot Key 20 (Judgement, Pluto) moves to the North face, attributed to Key 16 (The Tower, Mars), and to the South face attributed to Key 19 (The Sun, Sun). Since the North face of the Cube is related to activity and awakening and the South face of the Cube is related to enlightenment and growth, this coordinate relates to the inner impulse of life to move forward to liberation.

The angel of revelation, Gabriel, blows his trumpet (Key 20) to begin our awakening (Key 16). Eventually we are born again (Key 19) in the light of spiritual understanding. Meditate on this coordinate to help align personal activities with the Divine Will.

### Questions for contemplation:

1. How many symbols of transformation can be found in these Tarot Keys?

   A. Key 20
   B. Key 16
   C. Key 19
   D. Key 21

2. What associations do you have with Judgement?

   A. The Tower
   B. The Sun
   C. The World

3. What correlations can you make with the Hebrew letter Shin?
   A. Peh
   B. Resh

4. What are the astrological associations with Tarot Key 20?

   A. Key 16
   B. Key 19

5. What is the relationship between freedom, liberation, and this coordinate of the Cube of Space?

6. What relates this coordinate to the process of awakening?

7. What do these keys suggest about the process of enlightenment?

8. How does the element of fire manifest in each of these Tarot Keys?

   A. Key 21
   B. Key 20
   C. Key 16
   D. Key 19

Reflections:

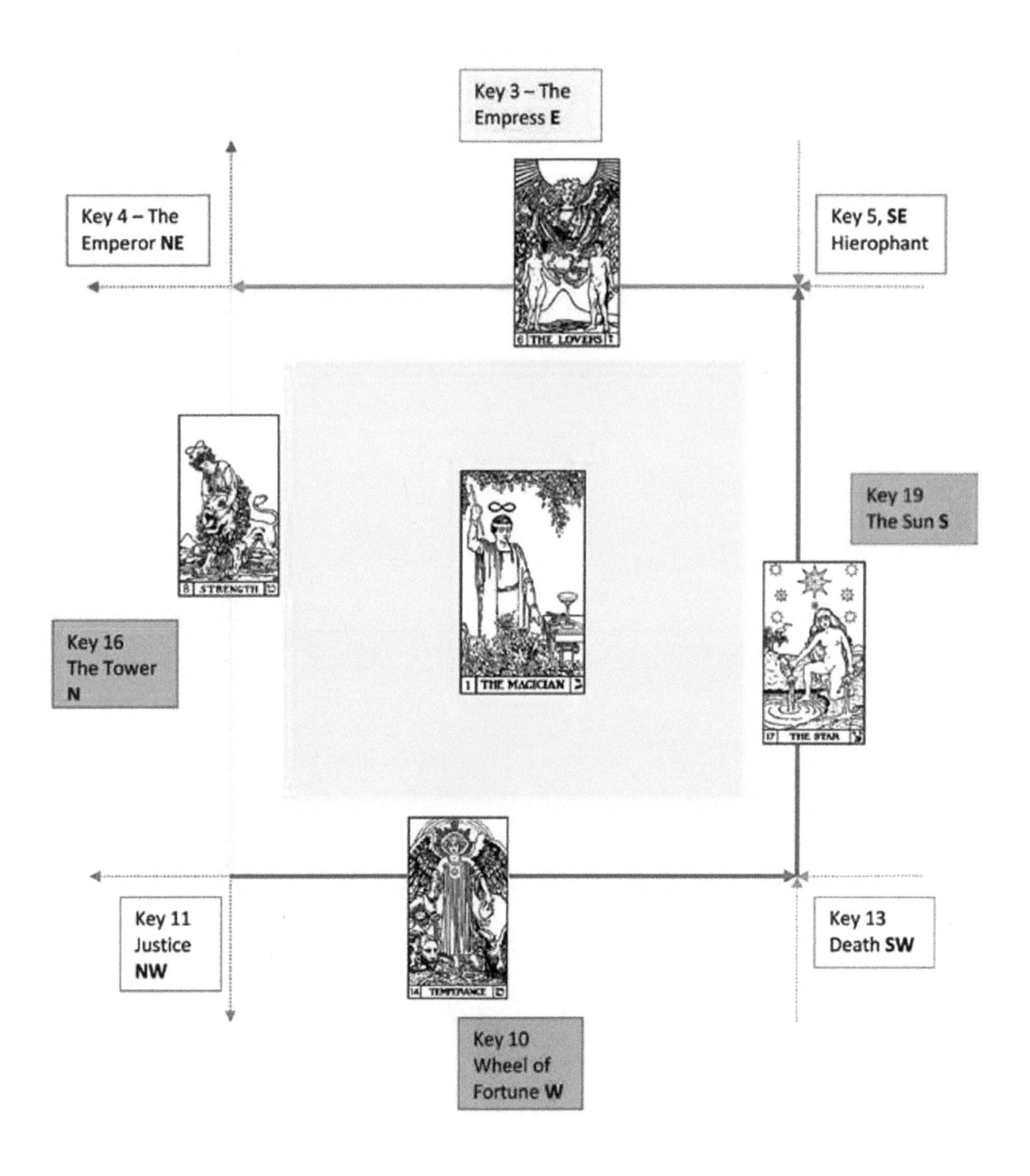


**Fig. 6**

The Above Face: The Magician – Mercury

## The Face of Self-Consciousness

The Above, or top, face of the Cube of Space is attributed to Tarot Key 1, and it represents self-conscious mental activity. The directional arrows on the sides of this face indicate a complete circuit flowing in a counter-clockwise direction. This represents the current of thought energy in the conscious mind, creating and interpreting the cycles and circumstances of our life. Meditate on this view of the Cube to enhance your ability to stay aware and awake in the present moment of your life.

### Questions for contemplation:

1. What associations do you have with The Magician?

   A. The Lovers
   B. Strength
   C. Temperance
   D. The Star

2. What correlations can you make with the Hebrew letter Beth?

   A. Zain
   B. Teth
   C. Samekh
   D. Tzaddi

3. What are the astrological correlations with Tarot Key 1?

   A. Key 6
   B. Key 8
   C. Key 14
   D. Key 17

4. How do the Tarot Keys bordering this face relate to the Magician?

   A. Key 1 to Key 6
   B. Key 1 to Key 8
   C. Key 1 to Key 14
   D. Key 1 to Key 17

5. How do Tarot Keys 6, 8, 14, and 17 relate to each other?

6. How does the quality of your attention and intention affect the operation of these Tarot Keys?

7. What does the progression from Tarot Key 6 to Key 8 to Key 14 to Key 17 to Key 6 tell you about self-conscious activity?

8. Does the flow of the current around this face suggest a circle or a spiral and why?

9. How does this face relate to life and death?

Reflections:

Throughout this workbook the reader will find that aspects of life are relevant to views of the Cube. Deeply meditating on these diagrams will bring out their relevance. For the next six sections, I am presenting some of the results of my study and meditation. There are many more ways to look at the Cube of Space. I challenge you to see how many interpretations you can find.

## Above Face—The Power of Presence

A common buzzword these days in spiritual and therapeutic circles is "mindfulness." If only we can become aware of the thoughts behind our actions, we can choose the actions that are most conducive to happiness. The attention and intention required for this is shown in the above face by Key 1, The Magician, and Mercury. This is also referred to as Presence, being fully aware in the present.

The control of action and energy that is the result of a clear intention is shown in North Above (Strength, Leo). In Key 8 the impulsive nature of the Mars force, our instinctual drives and our reactivity are being controlled by enlightened subconsciousness through the power of love. Emotions and drives are not being suppressed. They are in fact given a voice, but their expression is guided by love into constructive channels.

The Magician is acting as a channel for power from superconscious levels.

The self-conscious mind directs the power of divine love wherever it puts its attention. That's why attention increases whatever it focuses on, and the most important ingredient in showing love is quality attention. West-Above (Temperance, Sagittarius) shows the effect of presence on our outer circumstance. By being present to our environment, we find ways to temper our reactions to events so that we expand our personal skills and our capacity for love. We can also become sensitive to the spiritual truth and guidance hidden within our outer circumstances as we become more deeply aware.

The Star (Key 17, Aquarius) is associated with meditation. The dawning of enlightenment is the result of turning attention to the light of inner reality. As we "fish for truth" in the ocean of Reality, the quality of our attention and the steadiness of our mind will bring us deeper levels of awareness that increase our capacity to live in love and truth.

When a person becomes present to the angel's understanding of Reality as seen in Key 6 (The Lovers, Gemini) in East Above, the errors of the limited personal perspective can be changed by the greater truth that corrects the projections of the self-conscious mind. Then, the creative imagination forms images in accordance with truth, and the mind operates in harmony with the love and blessings of God.

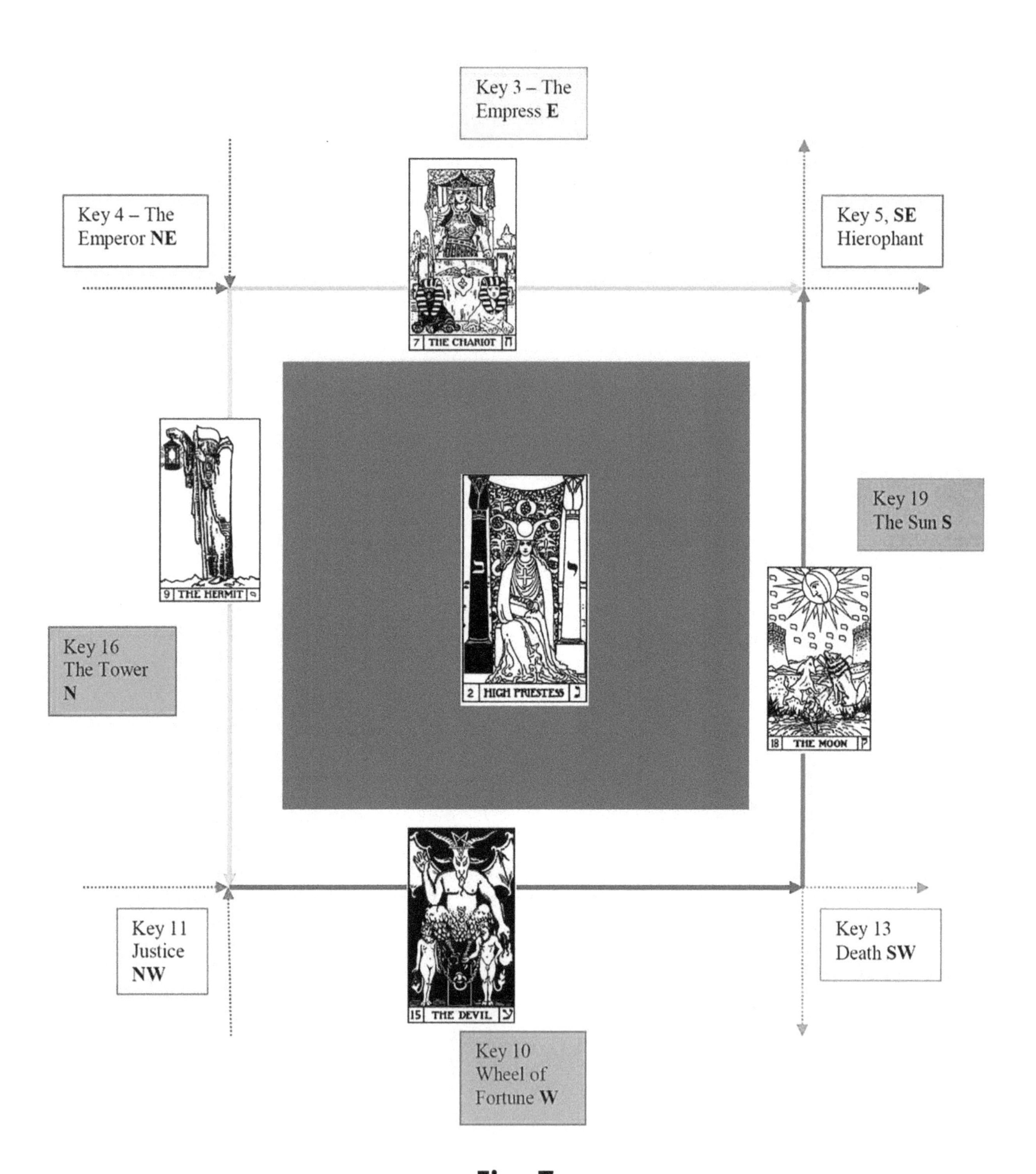


**Fig. 7**

The Below Face: High Priestess – Moon

## The Face of Subconsciousness

The Below, or bottom face of the Cube of Space is assigned to Tarot Key 2, and it represents subconscious mental activity. The current in the east and west flows from north to south. In the north, it flows from east to west and in the south, it flows from west to east. All of the diagonals ascend from the corners of this face. The Tarot Keys and Hebrew letters on this face immediately follow the sequence of the Tarot Keys on the Above face on the corresponding sides: EA-Key 6, EB-Key 7; NA-Key 8, NB-Key 9; WA-Key 14, WB-Key 15; SA-Key 17, SB-Key 18. Meditate on this view of the Cube to get in touch with your body awareness and the subtleties of your relationships.

### Questions for Contemplation:

1. How do the Tarot Keys on the edges of this face relate to subconscious mental activity?

2. What associations do you have with the High Priestess?

   A. The Chariot
   B. The Hermit
   C. The Devil
   D. The Moon

3. How many attributes can you associate with the Hebrew letter Gimel?

   A. Cheth
   B. Yod

C. Ayin
D. Qoph

4. How does this face relate to peace or strife?

5. What are the astrological correspondences with Tarot Key 2?

   A. Key 7
   B. Key 9
   C. Key 15
   D. Key 18

6. How do the Tarot Keys attributed to the boundaries of this face relate to the High Priestess?

   A. Key 2 to Key 7
   B. Key 2 to Key 9
   C. Key 2 to Key 15
   D. Key 2 to Key 18

7. How do Keys 7, 9, 15, and 18 relate to each other?

8. How does this face relate to embodiment including the human body and its activities?

9. If the North represents the unknown and the South enlightenment, what does the movement from north to south in this face suggest to you about the purpose of subconscious activity?

10. How does will and purpose relate to this face?

11. How is memory working in the operation of the Tarot Keys on this face?

Reflections:

## Below Face—The Power of Memory

The Cube of Space actually rests on this face. It is attributed to Key 2, High Priestess, Moon, and subconsciousness. Subconsciousness holds the "DNA of the universe." It's actually the working power that makes things happen. It takes the suggestions of the conscious mind and creates the pattern that produces a result.

Memory is understood as important in the functioning of our minds. We can function because of memory. We can be creative because memory holds our knowledge and experience so that we can put these ingredients together in new ways to create new possibilities. When disease or disability threatens memory, the loss is felt as a loss of usefulness, or even a loss of identity.

However, the essential memory held by the High Priestess goes deeper than the learnings and experiences of a particular lifetime.

The core thought that is held in our deep memory is "I am." This core memory is the basis of our existence, both for individual persons and all of creation. It is our ability to be aware of this core memory that makes us self-conscious creatures.

In East-Below, Key 7, The Chariot, Cancer, our memory provides the ingredients for the building of images in the creative imagination. We can therefore produce a home for the images that make up our self-image. This "home" is actually the personal identity that builds our ego. However, since The High Priestess is actually united with all Existence, that greater memory is available to correct our personal errors and bring us to identification with God, the source of our existence.

In North-Below, Key 9, The Hermit, Virgo, our actions are remembered so that new forms can be built. This is the source of our habits. Our personal habits create the circumstances of our lives and the character of our personality. Our collective habits create our culture and traditions. Our biological habits build our bodies. As we awaken, clear intentions supported by new ways of acting and thinking can change our habits and create new circumstances that are healthier and more loving.

In West-Below, Key 15 (The Devil, Capricorn) represents the conditions that result from the lifestyle we've lived. The image of The Devil represents our bondage to the habits of mind and body that enslave the unexamined life. Perhaps unexpectedly, this edge of the Cube can bring liberation as well as bondage. The cosmic memory of the cycles of life from the beginning of creation are contained in Jupiter, the West face.

Combined with the deep unifying memory of the High Priestess, cause and effect can be understood in a way that liberates us from the attachments that bind us. (Keys 11-15-13) In studying natural laws, science has liberated us from bondage to our superstitions. By seeing how our lives fit into a picture that is more than the personal circumstances of our present lives, we can liberate ourselves from paralyzing guilt, shame and blame while using spiritual principles to set liberating causes into motion. With laughter born of the contrast between appearance and Reality, we can begin the liberation process.

In South-Below (Key 18, The Moon, Pisces), the form is modified during sleep so that evolution takes place. Sometimes when dealing with an intractable problem, we are advised to "sleep on it." Often a period of deep sleep will bring the answer to our problem. (Keys 15-18-5). That is because the deep memory of the High Priestess can be accessed during sleep to bring us the enlightenment we need to solve our problem.

Enlightenment is a process, rather than an event. The Moon represents the process that incorporates our moments of realization so that moments of clarity and connection become integrated into our bodies and lifestyles. Then we can sustain higher consciousness instead of falling back into our old habits after brief moments of realization.

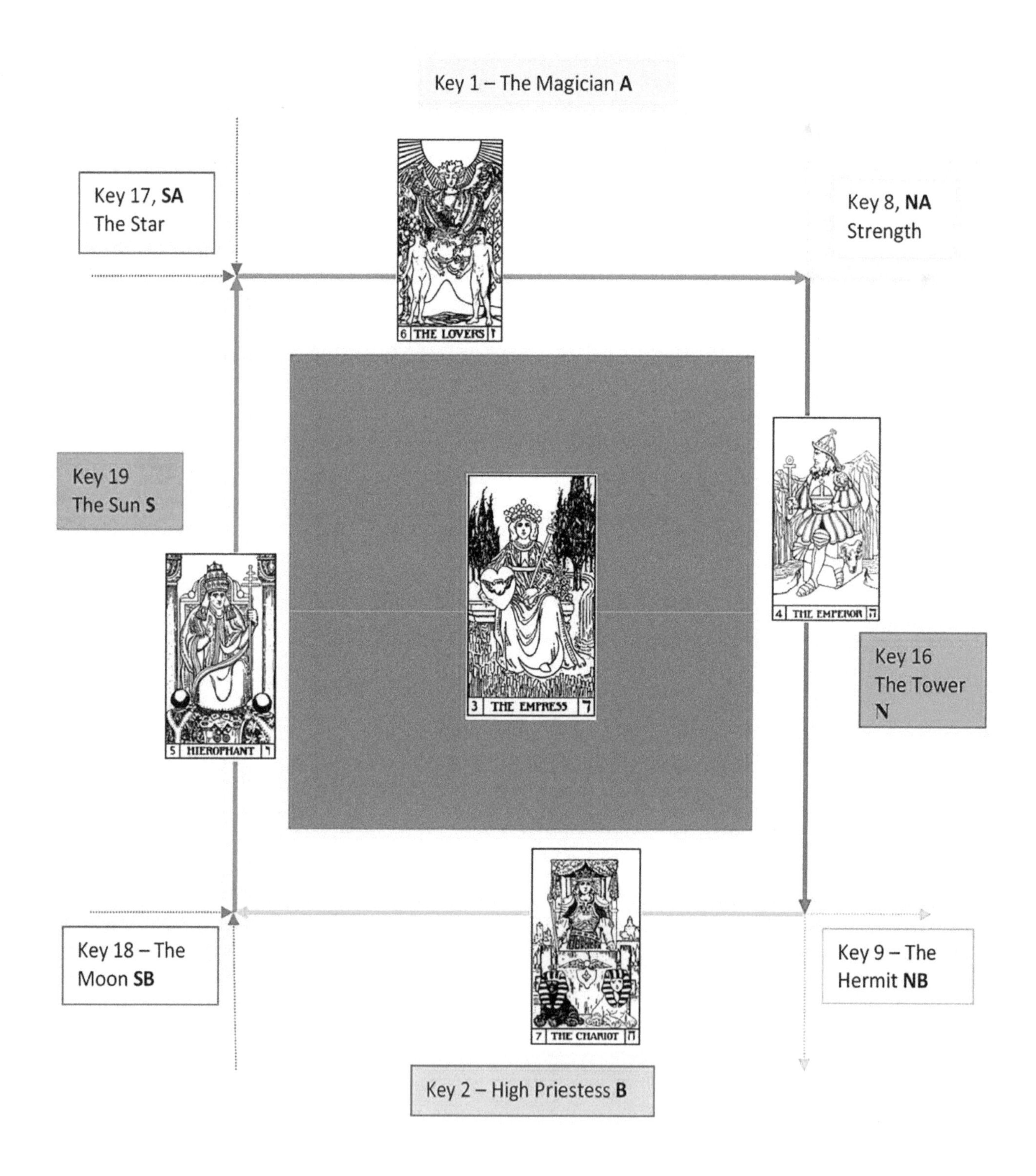


**Fig. 8**

The East Face: The Empress—Venus

## The Face of Creativity

The East face of the Cube of Space is attributed to Tarot Key 3, and it represents the creative mental activity of imagination. As with the Above face, the East face is a closed circuit of energy, this time flowing in a clockwise direction. Since the East-Above line joins these two faces you can visualize the movement of each of these faces as wheels whose gears turn each other at the line where they meet. Since both of these faces deal primarily with mental activity, they could be looked at as a diagram of how the mind goes around in circles. Meditate on this face to stimulate your creative efforts and enhance your spontaneity.

### Questions for contemplation:

1. How do each of the Tarot Keys on this face contribute to creative purpose?

   A. Key 3
   B. Key 4
   C. Key 7
   D. Key 5
   E. Key 6

2. What associations do you have with The Empress?

   A. The Emperor
   B. The Chariot
   C. Hierophant
   D. The Lovers

3. What are the correlations with the Hebrew letter Daleth?

   A. Heh
   B. Cheth
   C. Vav
   D. Zain

4. What are the astrological correspondences to Tarot Key 3?

   A. Key 4
   B. Key 5
   C. Key 6
   D. Key 7

5. How do the Tarot Keys associated with the boundaries of this face relate to The Empress?

   A. Key 3 to Key 4
   B. Key 3 to Key 5
   C. Key 3 to Key 6
   D. Key 3 to Key 7

6. What does the circular current on this face suggest about the operation of creative imagination?

7. How does love relate to this face of the Cube of Space?

8. How might the operation of a Tarot Key be affected by the influence of the Key whose current flows into it?

   A. Key 6 to Key 4
   B. Key 4 to Key 7

C. Key 7 to Key 5
D. Key 5 to Key 6

9. Why might this face be seen as the door to understanding the Cube of Space in manifestation?

10. How does this face relate to Wisdom and Folly?

11. How might this face be seen as both the beginning and end of each cycle of manifestation?

Reflections:

## East Face—The Power of Images and Creativity

Image is recognized as vital in our society. People worry about the image they project. Advertisers try to control the image you have of their product. Politicians hire people to control their image. People are concerned with their self-image. Self-esteem is recognized as essential to success. But how much of this obsession with image leads to happiness?

Examining the East face of the Cube of Space helps us understand what is really true about the images we hold and the imagination that creates them.

First, The Empress shows us that the images we hold bear abundant fruit. It doesn't matter whether our images are true or false. What matters is how clear they are and how deeply we believe them.

The North-East line is attributed to Aries and The Emperor. This Tarot Key (Key 4) is also associated with reason, vision, and the Constituting Intelligence. It shows that we act on what we believe to be true. Expanding our circumstances requires expanding our vision of possibility. If our personal understanding is in accordance with Reality, then each of the cycles of life experience expands our understanding. However, our actions will be frustrated by a larger reality to the degree that our personal understanding is based on error or fear. This frustration shows us our errors until we realize greater truth. The North-East line also relates to the importance of putting our ideas into action if we want to see them manifest.

When our intentions reach subconsciousness, our mind does its best to align with the predominate image that we believe is true. It is possible to be fully aware of one belief while holding contradictory beliefs deep within our mind. In that case what manifests will be the belief that most often guides our behavior. South-Below, attributed to Cancer and The Chariot (Key 7), is receptive to our will, and it builds the body we need to manifest our desires and protect our imaginings.

Once again, if our intention is in accordance with the Will of God and a reality that is loving and larger than our personal self-image, the work of the South-Below path is to protect us from influences that might harm us. On the other hand, if our intention is serving narrow self-interest and our beliefs are based on erroneous assumptions that color our imagination, what will be built will include defense mechanisms for our ego that protect us from facing our fears and attachments.

Every cycle of life experience and mental development brings us to a time when we are ready to listen to a teacher (Hierophant, Taurus, Key 5) who can reveal more truth to us. This teacher may come in the form of inner intuition, a person or a teaching of wisdom. This time of revelation shows us a new way to see life experience. This line represents the inner longing that causes us to seek liberation. When we get in touch with our Inner Teacher, the work of surrendering our personal ego position to the Voice of God has begun.

With new insight born of experience we can move into a new creative phase with more love and acceptance, symbolized by East-Above and The Lovers (Gemini, Key 6). A new cycle can begin with increased understanding of truth. The key to new insight is the willingness to look to the Angel for the truth rather than limiting ourselves to a personality perspective.

This face of the Cube of Space is the door to all possibilities. Choices to let fear and selfishness govern the mind lead to a life that is more constricted and less fulfilling. Choosing to align with truth and openness to love lead to greater fulfilment, creative freedom, and happiness.

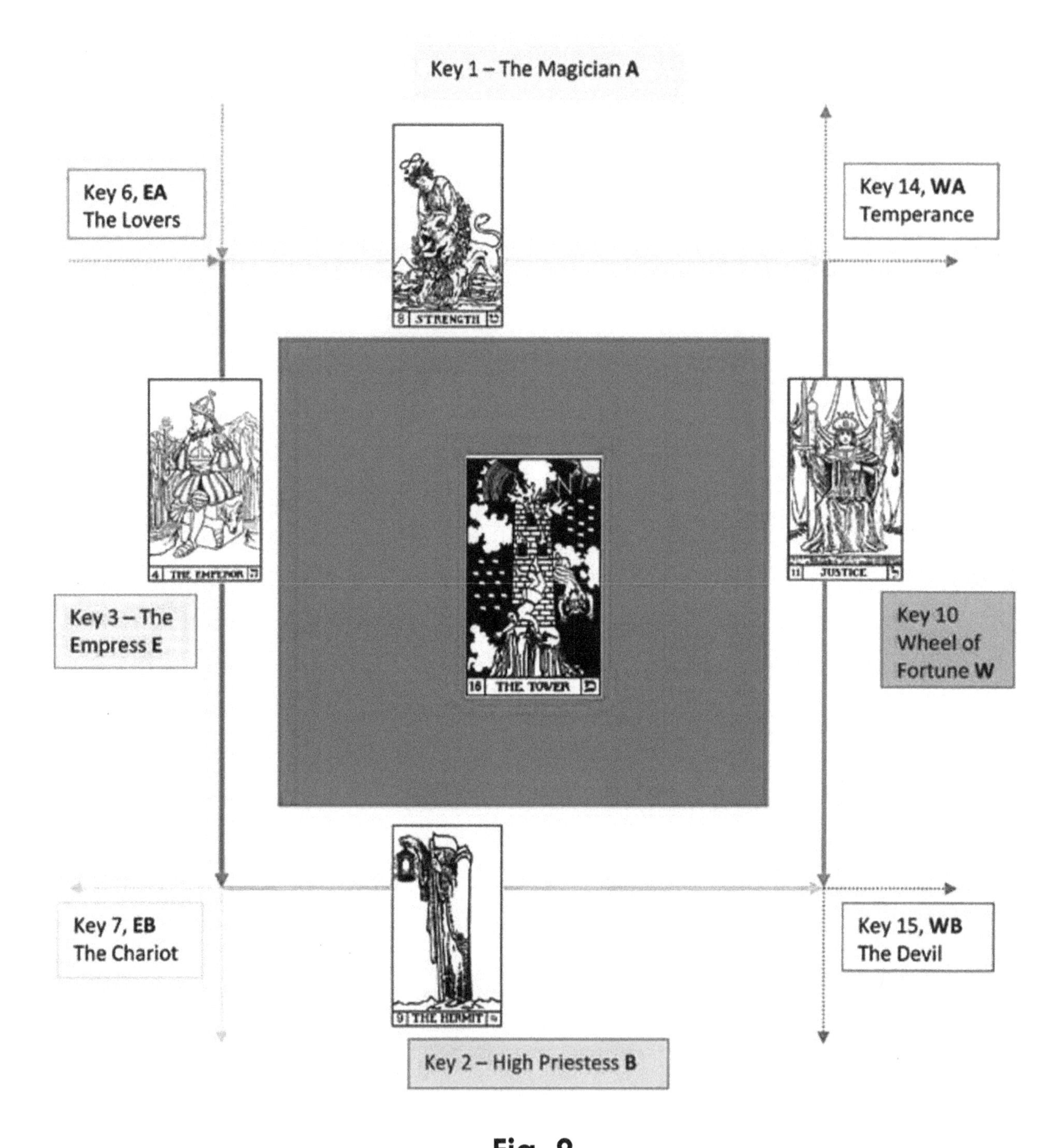


**Fig. 9**

The North Face: The Tower – Mars

## The Face of Action

The North face of the Cube of Space is attributed to Tarot Key 16, and it represents the action that carries our imaginings into manifestation. The directions of the currents in this face are from above to below and east to west. It is not until we take action that our assumptions are tested and our world begins to change. Meditate on this face to increase energy, overcome inertia, and stimulate the courage to act.

### Questions for contemplation:

1. What associations do you have with The Tower?

   A. The Emperor
   B. The Hermit
   C. Justice
   D. Strength

2. What are the correlations with the Hebrew letter Peh?

   A. Heh
   B. Yod
   C. Teth
   D. Lamed

3. What are the astrological correspondences to Tarot Key 16?

   A. Key 4
   B. Key 8
   C. Key 9
   D. Key 11

4. What relationships can you find between the Tarot Keys defining this face of the Cube of Space and Tarot Key 16?

   A. The relationship between Key 16 and Key 4
   B. Key 16 and Key 8
   C. Key 16 and Key 9
   D. Key 16 and Key 11

5. How do these Tarot Keys relate to the process of awakening?

6. What does the direction of the currents associated with this face suggest about the purpose of action?

7. North is the direction of greatest darkness, and it is associated with that which has not been experienced and is therefore unknown. What is the relationship between this aspect of the direction North and the process of awakening?

8. How does this face relate to Grace and Sin?

Reflections:

## North Face—The Power of Sexual Energy in Awakening

Sexual energy is so powerful that every society and system of morality spends a lot of effort to control and harness it. On the Cube of Space, the North face tells us a lot about the use of this energy.

The Tarot card on the north face is The Tower (Key 16). This card is associated with Mars, which in Roman mythology was associated with sexual energy, particularly masculine, projective sexuality. This is not limited to sexual expression, because the active life force used in sexual expression is the driving energy behind all action. When we look at this card, we see a picture of destruction. Every action destroys an old reality to create a new one. The Tower of ideas that supports the crown of our ego must eventually be destroyed if we are to be free from illusion.

Even the ordinary sexual expression of lovers makes the participants vulnerable to transformation as their individual egos and bodies must cooperate and surrender to one another in the act that is required to create another living being.

The North East side of this face is attributed to Aries (Key 4), which is ruled by Mars. It is the vision of The Emperor that gives purpose and direction to the life energy expressed in the North face. The Emperor wants to see the creative, loving energy symbolized by the East face actualized in form.

The North Above side is attributed to Leo and the Tarot card Strength (Key 8). Here, the divine feminine, which understands the principles of manifestation, controls the lion of sexual energy according to the desires of love. The mind that is controlled by love and truth guides all acts of power to accomplish the will of the creator.

The North Below side is attributed to Virgo and the Tarot card The Hermit (Key 9). There are some paradoxes in the symbols of this Tarot card. Virgo is the sign of the virgin. The divine creative substance symbolized by the below face of the Cube remains pure and virginal, no matter what form it takes in a particular creative expression, just as light remains pure no matter what it illumines.

However, coitus is also attributed to this symbol, because in North Below the creative substance responds to the action of the life power to form the new reality envisioned by the Emperor and suggested by the woman of Key

The North West side is attributed to Justice and Libra (Key 11). It is the place of relationship.

Creative sexual expression always requires a relationship. Bringing a vision into physical reality requires both action and response. Cause and effect must completely work out on all levels. Justice does not oppose grace and love, it provides the necessary container for love to manifest.

When Natural Law is fulfilled, manifestation occurs in the Western face. Love is the necessary requirement for positive use of sexual energy. The greater a person's capacity for love, the more liberation, enlightenment, and happiness the person finds in their life.

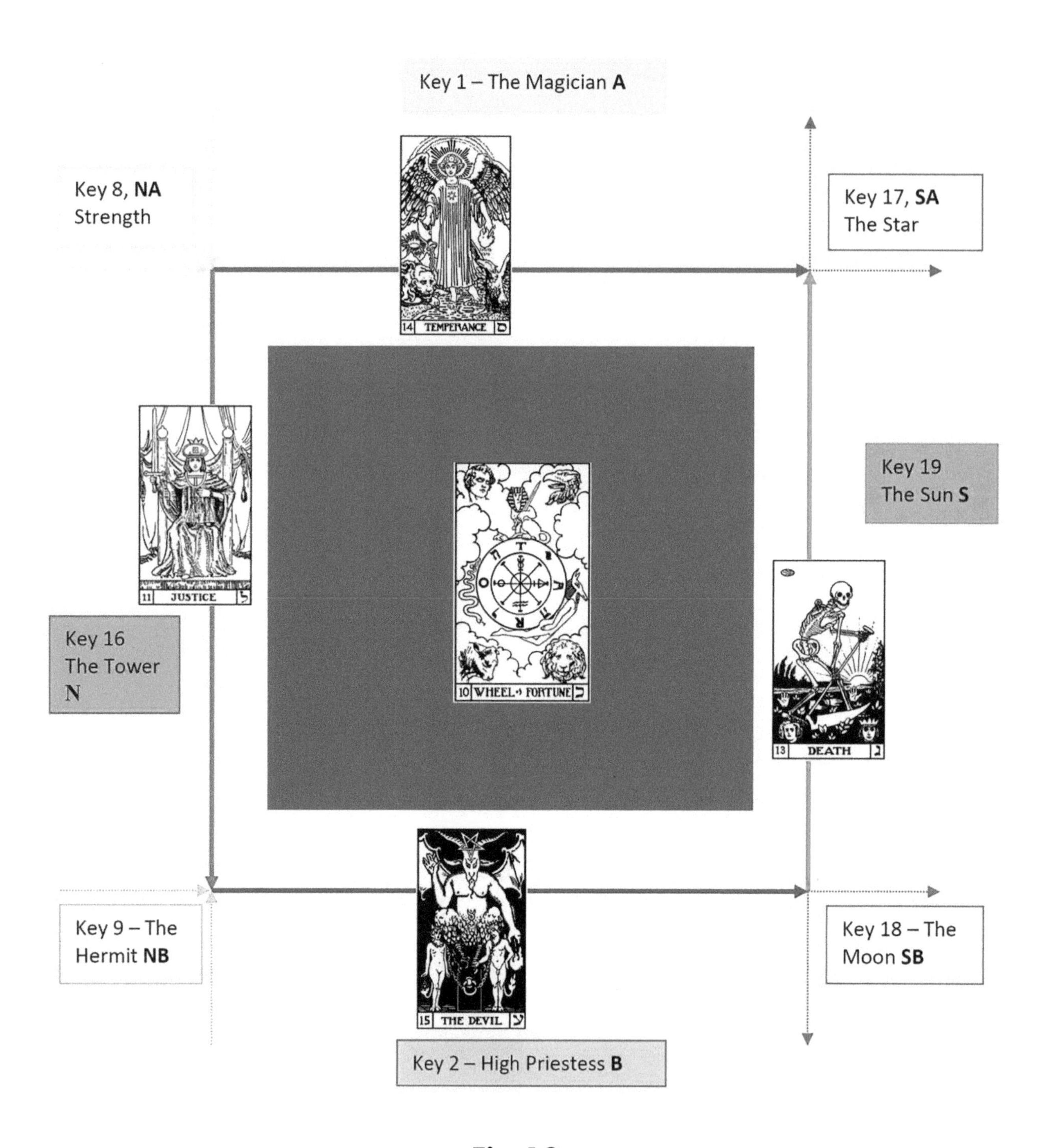


**Fig 10**

The West Face: Wheel of Fortune — Jupiter

## The Face of Outer Expression

The West face of the Cube of Space is attributed to Tarot Key 10, and it represents the outer circumstances of our life. The current of the above and below edges flows from north to south. In the north the current flows from above to below, and in the south the current flows from below to above. The circumstances we have created by our actions show us the effect of our behavior and confront us with the operation of natural law within which we live and work. Meditate on this face to get in touch with the relationship between cause and effect.

### Questions for contemplation:

1. What does the symbolism of this face reveal about the problems of evil and death in the world?

2. What associations do you have with the Wheel of Fortune?

   A. Justice
   B. Temperance
   C. The Devil
   D. Death

3. What can you correlate with the Hebrew letter Kaph?

   A. Lamed
   B. Samekh
   C. Ayin
   D. Nun

4. How do the outer circumstances of your life propel your spiritual growth?

5. What are the relationships between Temperance and The Devil and how do they relate to the outer circumstances of our lives and Key 10?

6. How do the workings of karma relate to this face?

7. Does Death refer to the end of a cycle in this context? Why or why not?

8. What are the astrological associations with these Tarot Keys?

   A. Key 10
   B. Key 14
   C. Key 11
   D. Key 15
   E. Key 13

9. How are the principles of expansion and contraction related to this face of the Cube of Space?

10. What is good fortune in relationship to this face and your life?

Reflections:

## The West Face – The Power of Work

Expanding our capacity—the West face is about the current circumstances of our life. In working with the challenges of our lives, we expand our capacities. The West face (Key 10) is attributed to Wheel of Fortune and Jupiter, which is expansive in nature. So, our life must be about expanding our possibilities both personally and in respect to life on this planet we inhabit. So, why do our circumstances often seem so restricted and difficult?

Note that the West Below line is attributed to Capricorn and The Devil (Key 15), ruled by Saturn, the great teacher who uses discipline to ensure that lessons are remembered. This is our outer circumstance. It is the result of our actions of the past, and it shows us the consequences of our lifestyle so that we can improve and grow.

Flowing into this edge is the law of cause and effect, karma, represented by Justice (NW, Libra, Key 11), and the physical results of our actions represented by North-Below, The Hermit (Virgo, Key 9). So, our circumstances include both the mental and physical body created by our past actions, and the people and relationships we've developed over time.

Our mission is not to stay bound, but to see through the illusions of our past and let go of the attachments that keep us bound. When our relationships are based on love, we are able to truly see the people in our life as they are. We are free when our love includes complete acceptance of ourselves and others.

To help us out we have a Holy Guardian Angel above us in the position of West-Above, (Temperance, Key 14). This angel holds our spiritual intention to travel through life and expand our consciousness (Sagittarius). We encounter this angel through teachers and teachings that give us access to bigger perspectives than we began life with. The resulting realizations and awakening break down our entrenched ego positions that keep us centered in our personal selves. The most important capacity this process expands is our capacity to love.

In order to expand our capacity to love beyond personal attraction that is filled with projections of our needs and desires, we must give up our patterns of attachment that keep us from fully loving another person as they are instead of the way we wish they were.

When a pattern is finished, it dies.

We transform and meet the spiritual presence of our guide, ready for more enlightenment. This happens in cycles great and small. Sometimes on the South-West side (Key 13, Scorpio, Death) death meets us as physical death at the end of a lifetime that can accomplish nothing more. Sometimes it's an ego death that readies us for a new cycle.

Always there's the death of an attachment that has kept us from seeing Reality as it is instead of as we want it to be. Each death brings us the possibility of more enlightenment and the opportunity to try again.

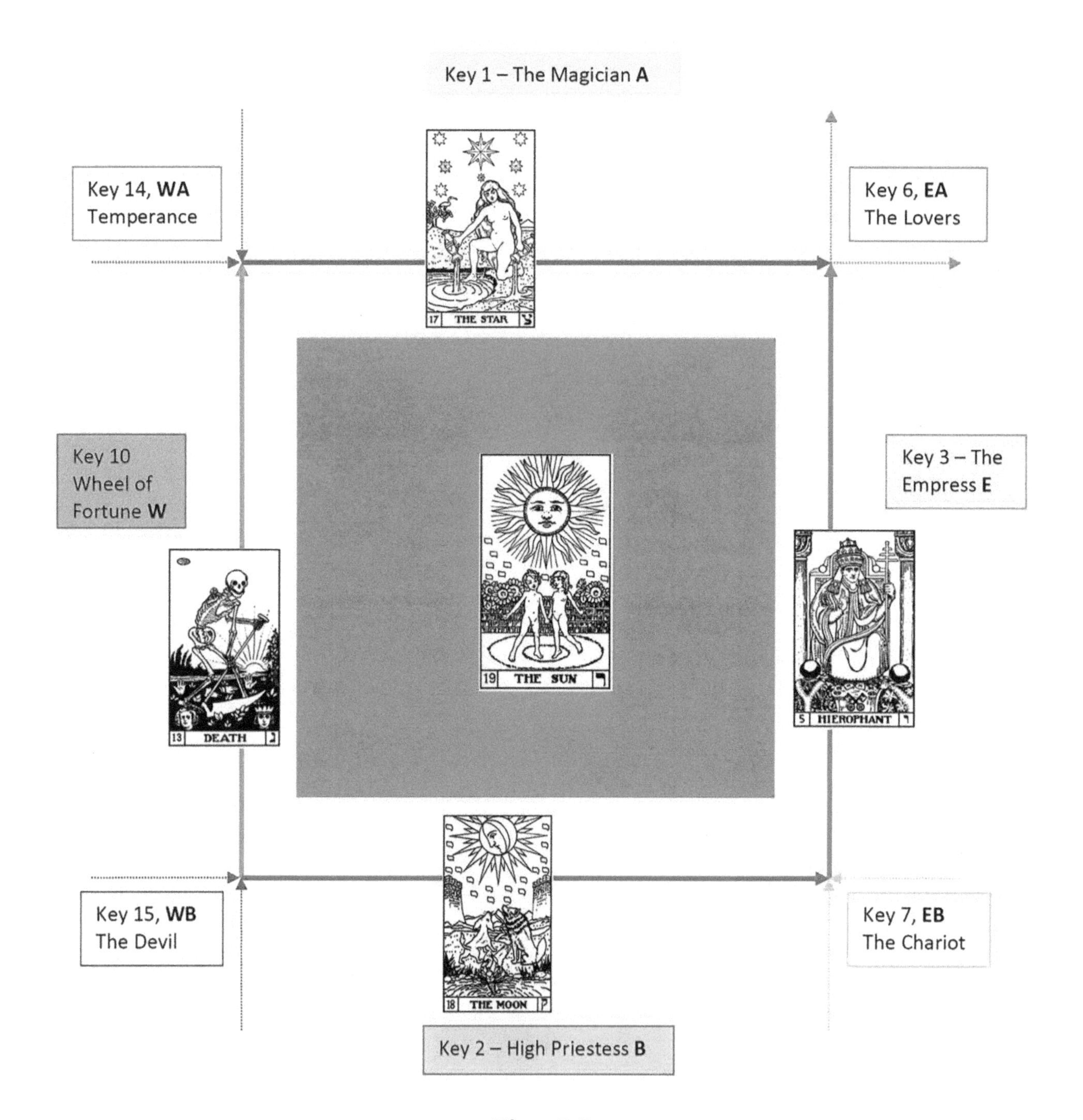


**Fig. 11**

The South Face: The Sun — Sun

## The Face of Enlightenment

The South face of the Cube of Space relates to the development of understanding and the realization of meaning and purpose in life. The current of energy in this face flows from west to east and below to above. In this face, the heart integrates the physical and mental results of our life experience to distill the truth that leads to liberation. Meditate on this face to deepen trust in the universal process of enlightenment.

### Questions for contemplation:

1. How is love experienced in this face?

2. What associations do you have with The Sun?

   A. Death
   B. The Star
   C. The Moon
   D. Hierophant

3. What are the astrological associations with The Sun?

   A. The Star
   B. The Moon
   C. Death
   D. Hierophant

4. What correlations can you make to the Hebrew letter Resh?

   A. Nun
   B. Tzaddi
   C. Qoph
   D. Vav

5. How many ways is light symbolized in the Tarot Keys associated with this face?

6. What images of sustenance and reproduction are found in these Tarot Keys?

7. What does the direction of the currents of energy in this face suggest about the nature of enlightenment?

8. Is Tarot Key 13 related to birth or death in relation to this face? Why?

9. What is suggested in this face of the Cube of Space about the relationship of meditation and sleep to enlightenment?

10. What do the Tarot Keys on this face suggest about the relationship between ego and intuition?

11. Who or what is controlling the processes taking place on this face of the Cube of Space?

12. What is being broken down and what is being built up in the process of regeneration?

Reflections:

## South Face—The Power of Faith and Love

When faith is mature your life is filled with light. The children in Tarot Key 19 are dancing through their life with complete trust in the sustaining light and life of The Sun. They are no longer disturbed by the opinions and illusions of the outer world around them because their mind and heart are open to the spiritual truth behind appearances. Their life is spent working to manifest the will of God in the world, because their vision of the truth is clear.

In the South-West edge of the Cube (Key 13, Death, Scorpio), they released the attachments that kept them from seeing Reality clearly.

The practice of meditation in South-Above (Key 17, The Star, Aquarius) is revealing truth to them in ever growing stages as their practice strengthens their mind and their ability to concentrate.

In South-Below (Key 18, The Moon, Pisces) they travel the path of return steadily as experience builds their bodies in accordance with truth. The wounds created by their experience in the outer world of illusion lose their power as love begins to dominate their life and transform their body and mind.

With faith and healing comes the ability to hear and understand the instructions of the Spiritual Teacher (South-East, Key 5, Hierophant, Taurus) who guides their progress toward realization. Liberation comes as the ego lets go of identifying with the personality and comes to realize that only in choosing the destiny of God's plan can true fulfilment be realized. When we are able to moment by moment realize and live into a life of truth, beauty, and love we are free, and nothing can disturb the peace at the core of our lives. What would our lives be like if we were able to be fully conscious of the truth of each moment? What if all of our decisions were based on the question, "What is the most loving thing to do and the most loving way to be in this moment?"

# THE EDGES OF THE CUBE OF SPACE

## WHERE THE FACES MEET — THE SIGNS OF THE ZODIAC

## How Big is Your Reality?

In this section of the workbook, each edge of the Cube of Space is examined in relation to the faces adjoining it and the direction of its flow. These are then related to the symbolism of the Tarot Keys associated with the faces and the edges between them.

The order followed is numerical, alphabetical (in Hebrew) and astrological. This results in an examination of the boundaries of the East face, followed by the North face, the West face, and then the South face, with the Above and Below faces looked at alternately.

This section provides an in-depth look at the single letters of Hebrew, their corresponding Tarot cards, and the signs of the zodiac. Attention is also given to the planetary influences that come together at each edge of the Cube of Space. The two planets on adjoining faces and the sign associated with the edge between them and their related Tarot Keys are then interpreted in terms of their relationship to cycles of human life.

This presentation emphasizes the relationship of the Cube of Space to our inner and outer life. This reveals the way the different aspects of our mind and experience work together to create the possibility of evolution and growth.

By understanding this experience, we increase our capacity for truth and love. Each expansion of awareness increases the size of our "personal Cube," our perception of the reality we live in.

As we grow, we move from a life feeling "boxed in" by the circumstances of our limited conditioning, towards a full acceptance of the reality of our potential.

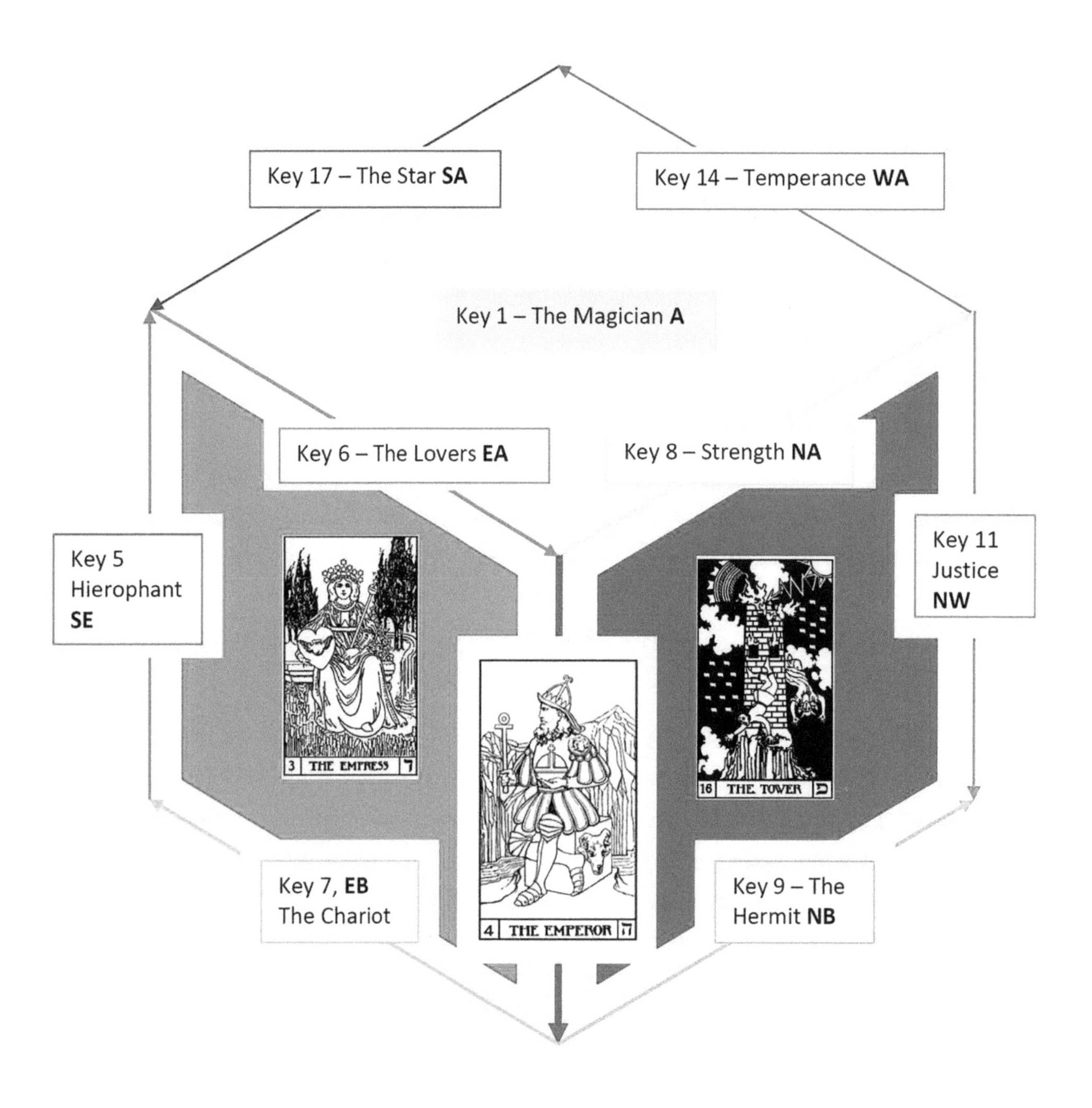


**Fig. 12**

The North East Edge: The Emperor— Aries

## Getting Started

The North-East line of the Cube of Space relates to the beginning of any cycle of manifestation. Its direction of flow is from above to below. The size of the Cube is infinite until this first defining line is drawn, separating an inside from an outside. The vision of the Emperor (Key 4) stimulates new creative possibilities (Key 3) until we are ready to destroy the previous limitations (Key 16) so that new possibilities can grow. Meditate on this view to expand your vision and clarify your reasoning.

### Questions for contemplation:

1. Can you see the relationship between Tarot Key 4, the size of the Cube of Space as a whole and the nature of vision?

2. What associations do you have with The Emperor?

   A. The Empress
   B. The Tower

3. What are the correlations with the Hebrew letter Heh?

   A. Daleth
   B. Peh

4. What are the astrological attributions for Tarot Key 4?

   A. Key 3
   B. Key 16

5. What are the relationships between Tarot Key 4 and Key 16?

6. The relationships between Key 4 and Key 3

7. Tarot Keys 3, 16, and 4 to each other.

8. How does reason relate to these Tarot Keys and this side of the Cube of Space?

9. Why are the types of activity suggested by these Tarot Keys needed at the beginning of a cycle?

10. How does self-image relate to these Tarot Keys?

11. How do these Tarot Keys relate to our understanding of reality?

12. How does the element of fire relate to these Tarot Keys?

13. What does the direction of the flow of the North-East line tell us about the reasoning process?

Reflections:

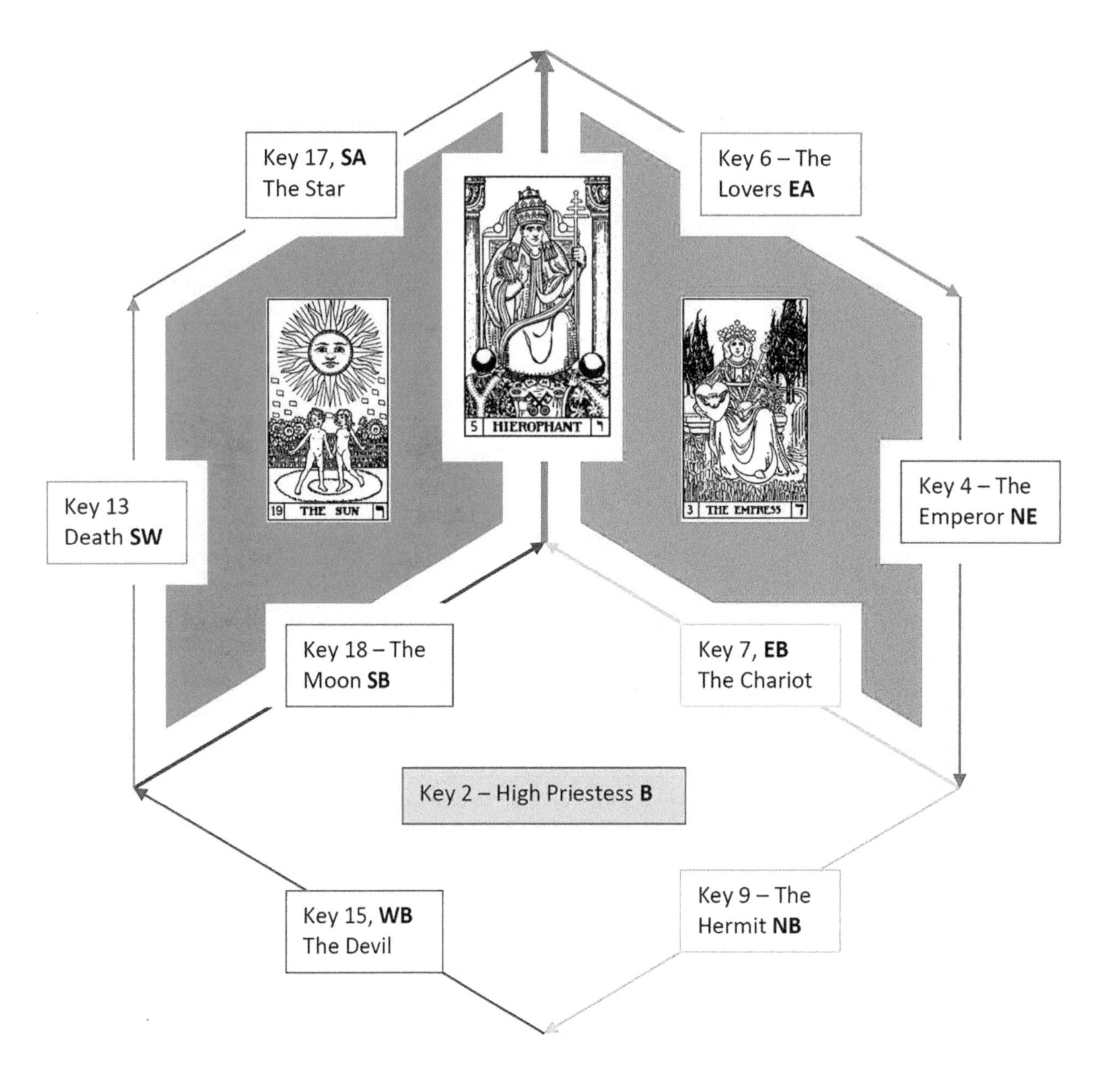


**Fig. 13**

The South-East Edge: The Hierophant— Taurus

## Praying for Guidance

The South-East side of the Cube of Space relates to the process of drawing from past experience and divine wisdom the resources necessary for creating anew. The direction of its flow is from below to above. As we practice trusting in the loving care of the universe (Key 19) our mental imagery (Key 3) is aligned with universal truth. We can then find reliable guidance in our intuition (Key 5). Meditate on this view of the Cube to expand your perspective of life experience to include the guidance of the Inner Teacher.

### Questions for contemplation:

1. What does the Hierophant reveal to us about our relationship to a spiritual teacher?

2. What associations do you have with the Hierophant?

   A. The Sun
   B. The Empress

3. What are the meanings associated with the Hebrew letter Vav?

   A. Resh
   B. Daleth

4. What are the astrological attributions associated with Tarot Key 5?

   A. Key 3
   B. Key 19

5. How does Tarot Key 5 relate to Key 3?

6. Key 5 to Key 19

7. Tarot Keys 19, 3 and 5 related to each other.

8. What does the direction of the flow of current in this line suggest about the nature of intuition?

9. How do these Tarot Keys relate to the process of enlightenment?

10. How many types of love are illustrated in these Tarot Keys?

11. What is the practical usefulness of the Hierophant and how does this relate to the use made of The Sun and The Empress?

12. How does the element of earth relate to this side of the Cube of Space?

13. How does this side of the Cube of Space reveal a relationship between unity and resources?

Reflections:

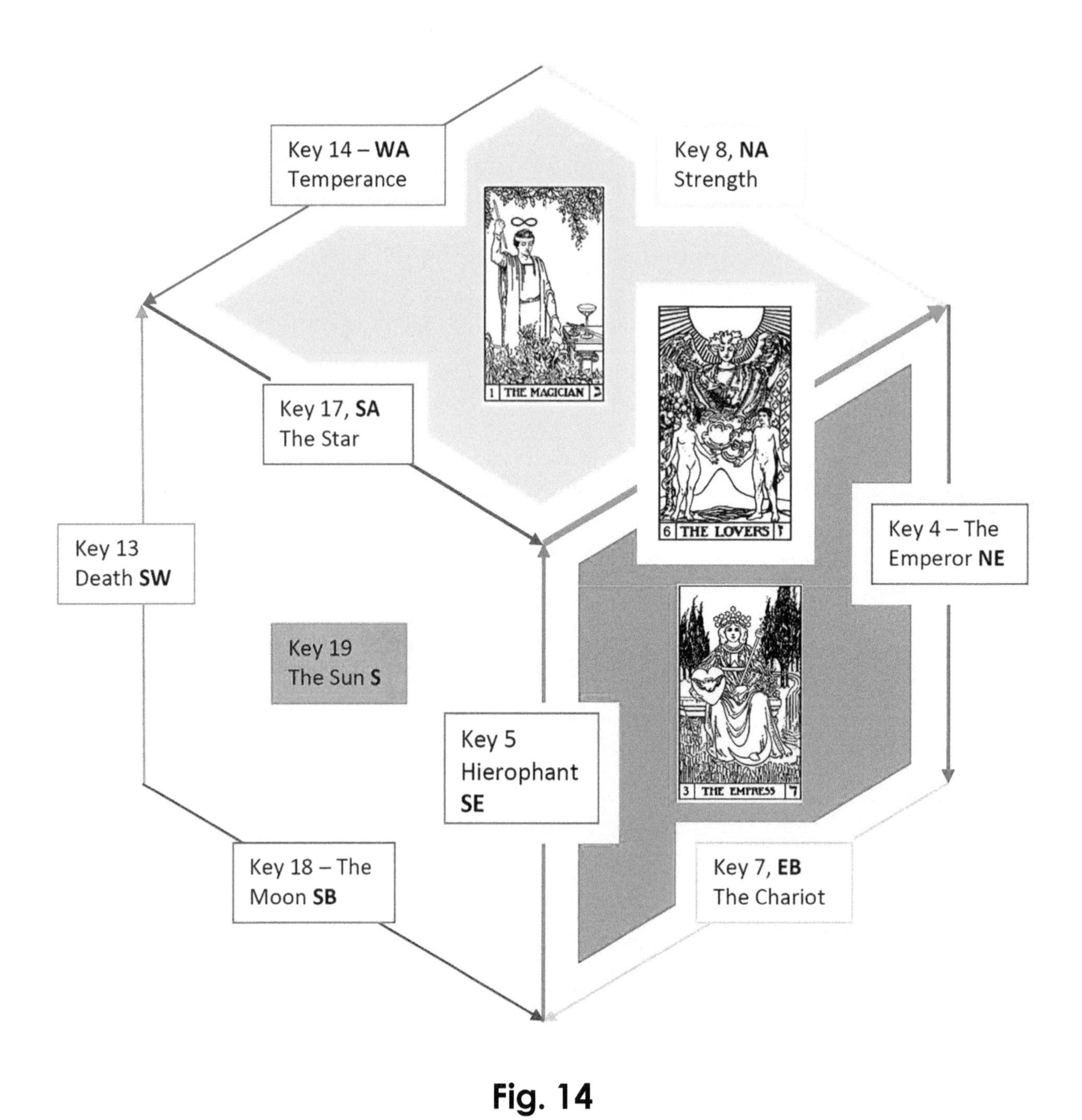


**Fig. 14**

East-Above Edge: The Lovers—Gemini

## Analyzing Your Options

The side of East-Above is the transition point between cycles on the Cube of Space. Here, the realization and experience of the past join with a new creative impulse, bringing conscious clarity of purpose into a new cycle of expression. When we are present and aware (Key 1) to the images in our mind (Key 3) we can choose to follow our spiritual truth and live with discrimination (Key 6). The current travels from south to north. Meditate on this view of the Cube to clear the mind before making a decision.

### Questions for contemplation:

1. Why would a path of transition be called The Lovers?

2. Who are the Lovers in this Tarot Key?

3. What associations do you have with The Lovers?

   A. The Magician
   B. The Empress

4. What are the correlations with the Hebrew letter Zain?

   A. Beth
   B. Daleth

5. What are the astrological associations with Tarot Key 6?

   A. Key 1
   B. Key 3

6. How does Tarot Key 6 relate to Key 1?

7. Key 6 related to Key 3

8. Keys 6 and 1 and 3 to each other

9. How do the figures in Tarot Key 6 relate to each other and to the adjoining faces of the Cube of Space?

10. How does Tarot Key 6 relate to the South side of the Cube of Space?

11. What does Tarot Key 6 tell us about discrimination and discernment and how does this principle relate to the surrounding Keys?

12. What does Tarot Key 6 and its position on the Cube of Space reveal about communication?

13. How are these Tarot Keys related to the element of air?

Reflections:

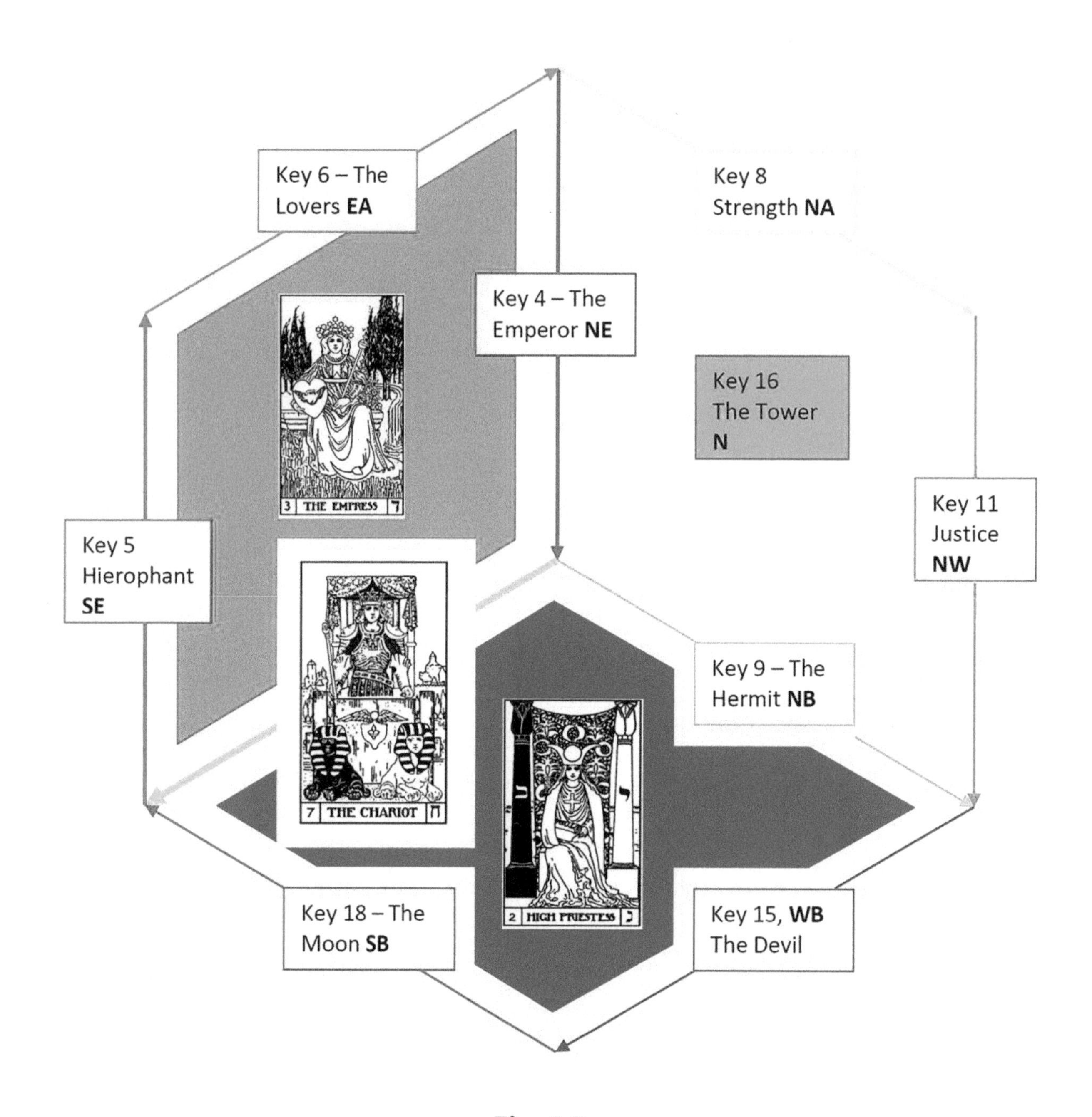


**Fig 15**

East-Below Edge: The Chariot—Cancer

## What Do You Really Want?

The side of East-Below is the path on the Cube of Space through which we become receptive to the will-power that defines and propels our goals and desires. The current in this line goes from north to south. All that we need is available in the unity of being (Key 2). From this infinite supply, we form the creative imagery that sets a pattern for our life (Key 3). In this process we are guided by the inner Self that builds the appropriate body and defines the field of our particular work (Key 7). Meditate on this view of the Cube to remember your true Self and your purpose in life.

### Questions for contemplation:

1. What do the symbols in Tarot Key 7 and its position on the Cube of Space suggest about the nature of will-power?

2. What associations can you make with The Chariot.

   A. The Empress
   B. The Moon

3. What corresponds to the Hebrew letter Cheth?

   A. Daleth
   B. Gimel

4. What are the astrological associations with Tarot Key 7?

   A. Key 2
   B. Key 3

5. How does Tarot Key 7 relate to Key 2?

6. Key 7 to Key 3

7. Tarot Keys 7 and 2 and 3 to each other.

8. How are these Tarot Keys related to receptivity?

9. How are these Tarot Keys related to establishing boundaries?

10. What does the direction of the current from north to south suggest about receptivity?

11. How is the element of water related to these Tarot Keys?

12. How do these Tarot Keys relate to the human body?

13. What evidence of power do you see in these Tarot Keys?

14. How do these Tarot Keys relate to home and family?

15. What does the position of The Chariot reveal about the nature of speech?

Reflections:

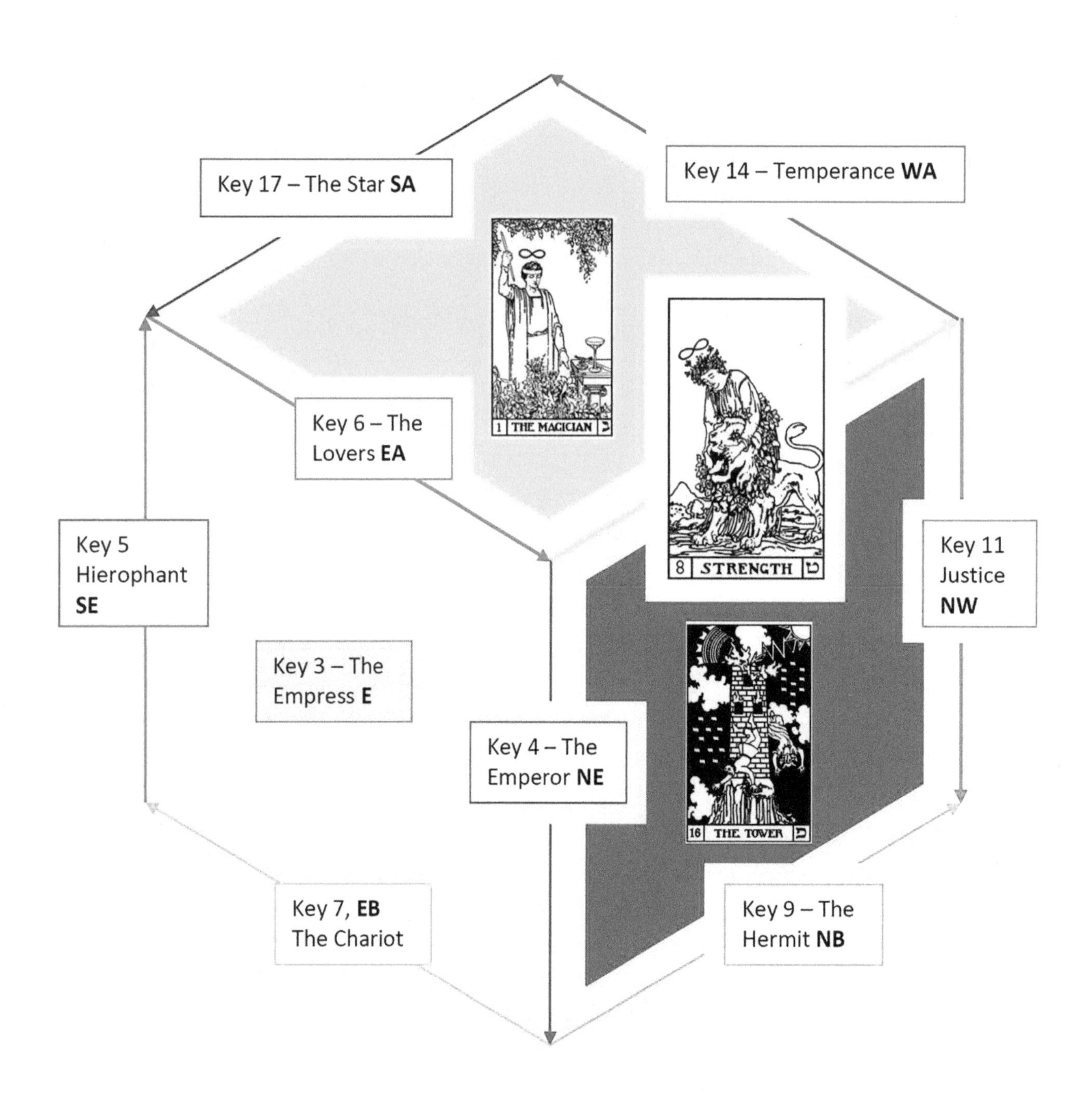


**Fig. 16**

North-Above Edge: Strength—Leo

## Taking Action

The North-Above line is about directing your energies to accomplish your goals. The direction of the current of energy is from east to west. Spirited intentional action partakes of the essence of this path. A person who becomes aware of being a channel for spiritual energy (Key 1) awakens from their tower of separation (Key 16) and learns to direct their vital energy with love (Key 8). Meditate on this view of the Cube of Space to overcome fear and act with courage and strength.

### Questions for contemplation:

Sometimes when an individual strives for something that would seem to be beyond his capacity, we use the expression "he has heart."

1. How does that expression relate to the symbolism of Tarot Key 8 and its position on the Cube of Space?
2. What associations do you have with Strength?
3. The Magician?
4. The Tower?
5. What are the correspondences with the Hebrew letter Teth?

A. Beth
B. Peh

6. What are the astrological attributes of Tarot Key 8?

   A. Key 1
   B. Key 16

7. How does Tarot Key 8 relate to Key 1?

8. Key 8 to Key 16

9. Keys 8 and 16 and 1 to each other

10. What symbols of fire are found in these Tarot Keys?

11. What is the relationship between The Empress and the female figure in Tarot Key 8?

12. How is the power of suggestion related to the operation of this side of the Cube of Space?

13. What do the roses mean and where do they come from?

14. How is love related to the activity of these Tarot Keys?

15. What is implied about the ego in the operation of these Tarot Keys?

16. How is the mouth related to the expression of the ego?

17. How do the colors used in these Tarot Keys reveal the relationships between them?

18. How does the direction of flow from east to west relate to goal-oriented activity?

19. What is the source of strength for the activity of Tarot Key 8?

Reflections:

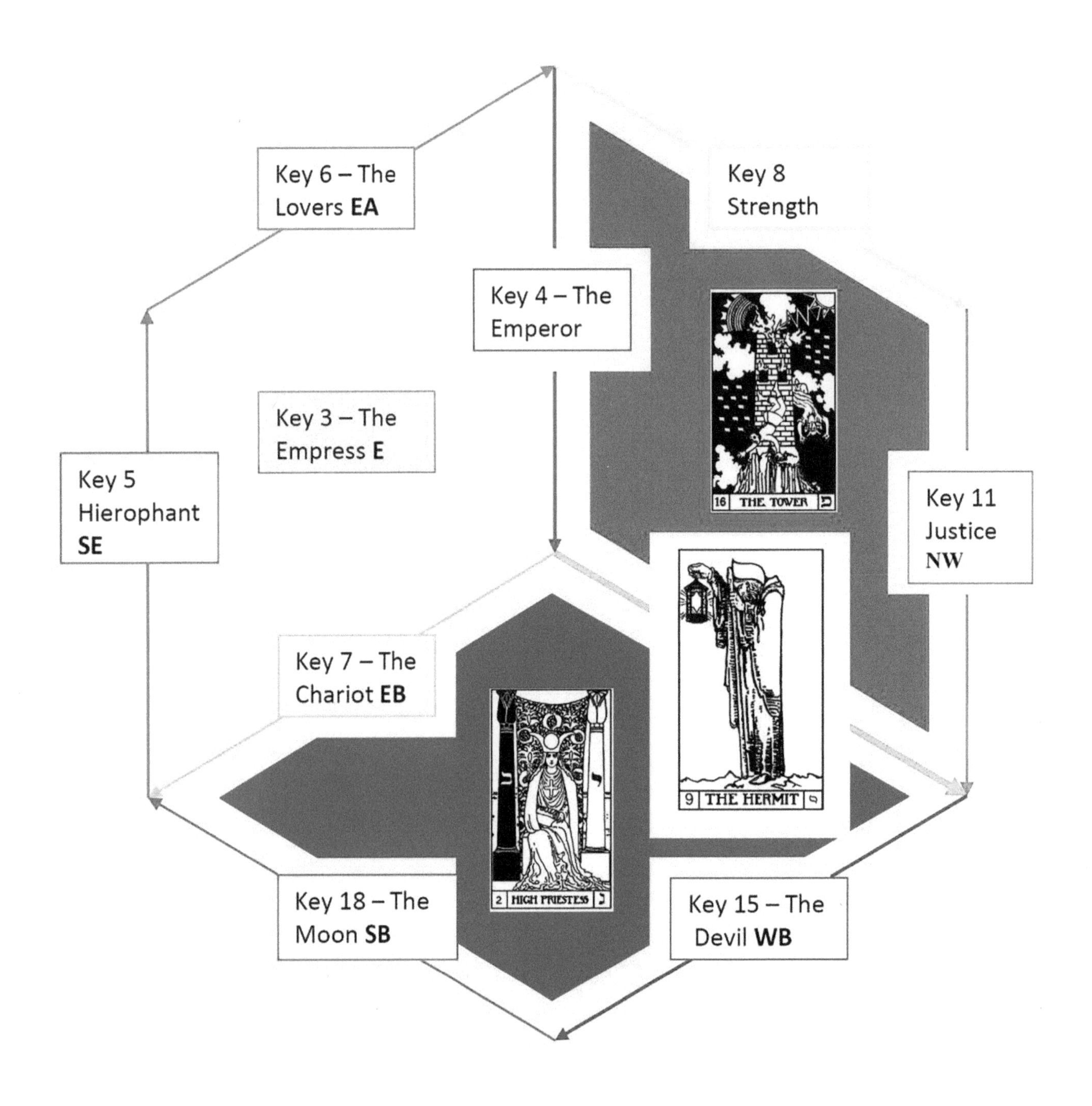


**Fig. 17**

North-Below Edge: The Hermit—Virgo

## Working-out the Details

The line of North-Below represents the responsiveness of life, working itself out in all the details of manifestation, according to the will-power expressed in each cycle of action. The direction of the flow of current is from east to west. To be in touch with the essential pattern of unity underlying that responsiveness, is to see the end, even in the beginning, of an endeavor. When we remember (Key 2) that there is only One Actor (Key 9) in every endeavor, we awaken (Key 16) from the illusion of our separation. Meditate on this view of the Cube of Space to become more sensitive to the best course of action in each present moment.

### Questions for contemplation:

1. Who is the guide for the action represented by this side of the Cube of Space?

2. What associations does The Hermit have for you?

   A. High Priestess
   B. The Tower

3. What attributions are associated with the Hebrew letter Yod?

   A. Gimel
   B. Peh

4. What are the astrological attributions of Tarot Key 9?

A. Key 2
B. Key 16

5. What relationships do you find between Tarot Key 9 and Key 16?

6. Key 9 and Key 2

7. Key 9 and Keys 2 and 16 to each other

8. What do these Tarot Keys reveal about the source of will and the nature of response?

9. What do the Yod symbols in these Tarot Keys suggest?

10. How are these Tarot Keys related to the body?

11. How is the subconscious process related to destruction and creation shown in these Tarot Keys?

12. What are the practical uses of the Tarot Keys related to this view of the Cube of Space?

13. How does the element of earth relate to this view of the Cube of Space?

Reflections:

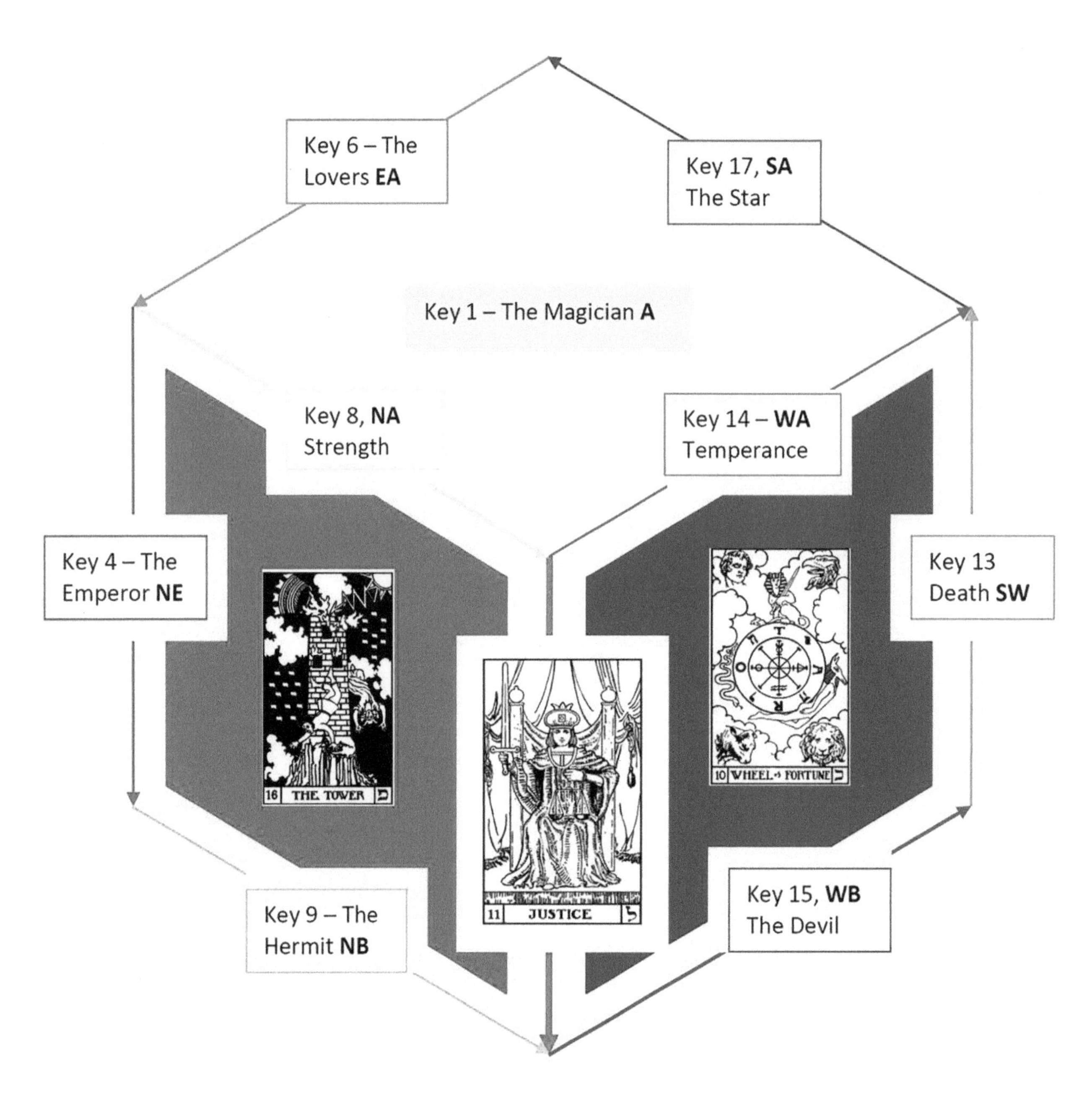


**Fig. 18**

North-West Edge: Justice—Libra

## Achieving Balance

Actions bring results. The North-West line is about the adjustments necessary to accommodate a new reality. The direction of flow is from above to below. Just relationships are necessary to a beautiful result in the world. As we awaken (Key 16) to the realization of undeviating justice (Key 11) in every circumstance of our lives (Key 10), we realize our power to work and assume responsibility for our circumstances. Meditate on this view of the Cube of Space to find the proper balance between work and relationships.

### Questions for contemplation:

1. How is love related to this view of the Cube of Space?

2. What associations do you have with Justice?

   A. Wheel of Fortune
   B. The Tower

3. What attributes are associated with the Hebrew letter Lamed?

   A. Kaph
   B. Peh

4. What are the astrological associations with Tarot Key 11?

   A. Key 10
   B. Key 16

5. How does Tarot Key 11 relate to Key 16?

6. Key 11 to Key 10

7. Tarot Keys 11 and 10 and 16 to each other

8. How does Tarot Key 1, The Magician, relate to Key 11, Justice?

9. How do the implements in Key 11 relate to the activity of Keys 16 and 10?

10. How is the mental quality of adjustment suggested in these Tarot Keys?

11. What is the meaning of karma as revealed in these Tarot Keys?

12. What do these Tarot Keys reveal about the nature of justice?

13. What does the direction of flow in this path reveal about the principles of balance, equilibrium, and justice?

14. How is the element of air significant to this view of the Cube of Space?

Reflections:

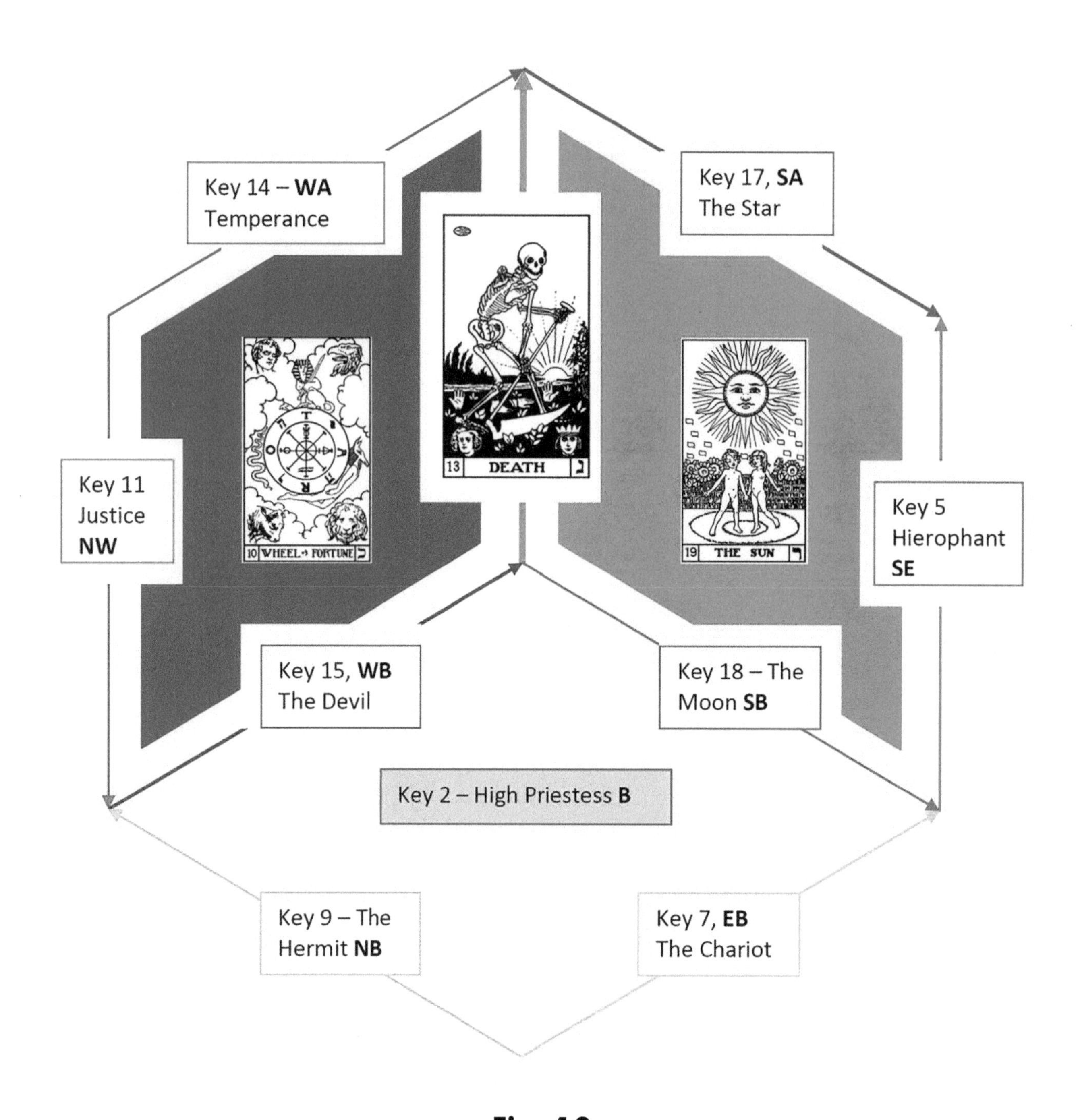


**Fig. 19**

South-West Edge: Death—Scorpio

## The Power of Transformation

In the line of South-West, the generative power destroys the old condition to create something new. The flow of this line is from below to above. This is really a place of liberation, as attachments to forms must be released for their true significance to be realized. Every cycle of our lives (Key 10) must end (Key 13). Every ending requires letting go of the past. However, every experience teaches us something that brings us closer to enlightenment (Key 19). Meditate on this view of the Cube of Space to help with the release of attachments that hinder the surrender necessary to live joyfully as spiritual beings.

### Questions for Contemplation:

1. How is life served by change as it is symbolized from this view of the Cube of Space?

2. What associations do you have with Death?

   A. Wheel of Fortune
   B. The Sun

3. What attributions are assigned to the Hebrew letter Nun?

   A. Kaph
   B. Resh

4. What are the astrological attributions assigned to Tarot Key 13?

   A. Key 10
   B. Key 19

5. How does Tarot Key 13 relate to Key 19?

6. Key 13 to Key 10

7. Keys 13 and 10 and 19 to each other

8. How are these Tarot Keys related to reproduction and regeneration?

9. What does the direction of the current in this line imply about change?

10. What is suggested by the symbols for turning in these Tarot Keys?

11. How are light and love symbolized in these Tarot Keys?

12. How is growth and movement indicated in these Tarot Keys?

13. How is the element of water related to this view of the Cube of Space?

Reflections:

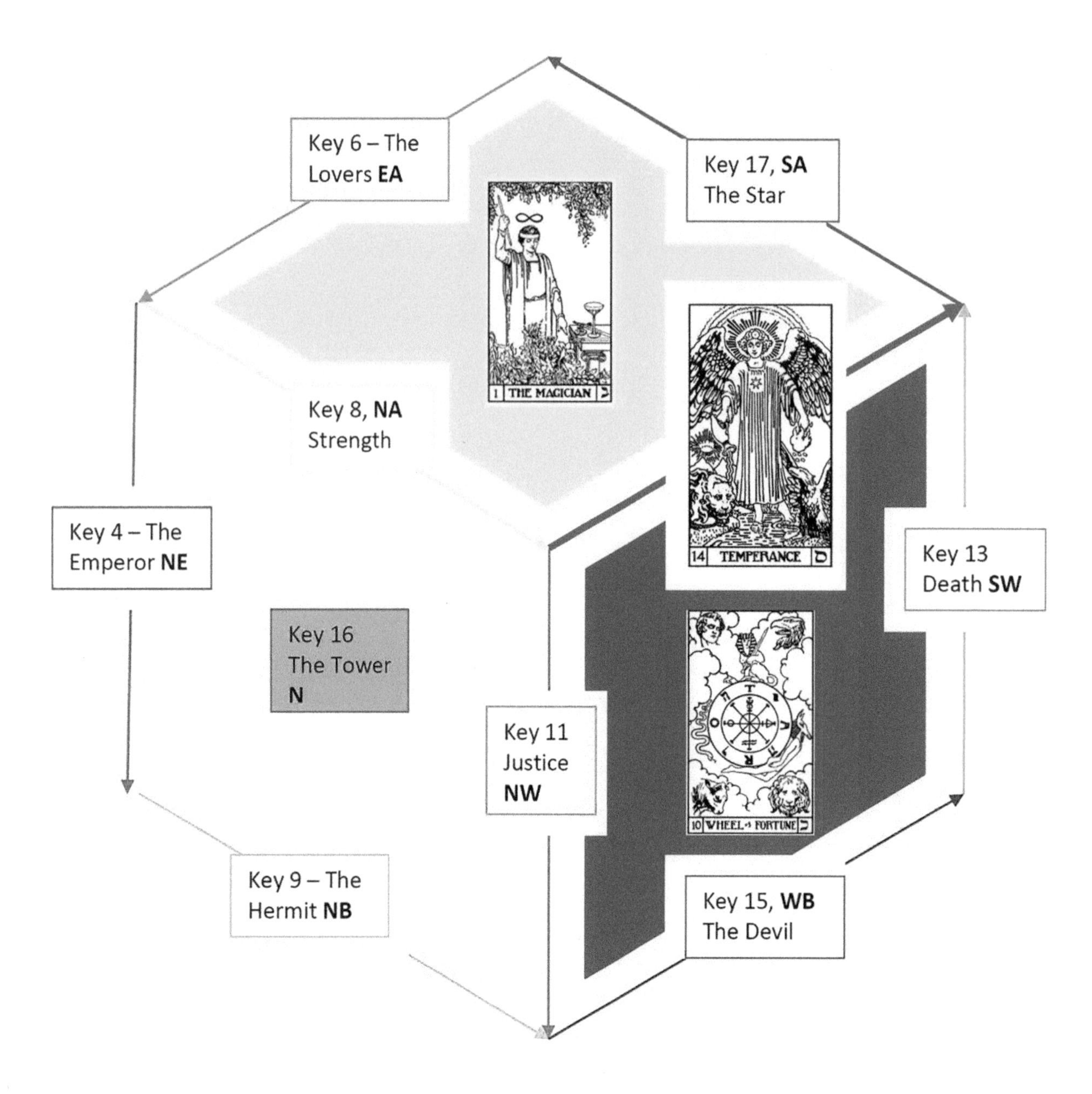


**Fig. 20**

West-Above Edge: Temperance — Sagittarius

## Do You Really Want It?

The line of West-Above is about the tests and transmutations involved in creating a new condition. The current in this line goes from north to south. The positive attitude that comes from spiritual awareness develops flexibility and strength in us as we deal with the circumstances of our lives. When we become present and aware (Key 1) of the cyclic patterns of our life (Key 10), we are able to recognize the work of Spirit (Key 14) purifying and transforming our soul in every circumstance of our lives. Meditate on this view of the Cube of Space to attune yourself with your Holy Guardian Angel and develop the habit of gratitude for the gifts of life.

### Questions for contemplation:

In trying to remain true to our ideals as we deal with our work in the outer world, we come to know the true nature of our desires.

1. What does Tarot Key 14 suggest about this process?

2. What associations do you have with Temperance?

   A. Wheel of Fortune
   B. The Magician

3. What are the attributes assigned to the Hebrew letter Samekh?

   A. Kaph
   B. Beth

4. What are the astrological correspondences with Tarot Key 14?

   A. Key 10
   B. Key 1

5. How does Tarot Key 14 relate to Key 10?

6. Key 14 to Key 1

7. Keys 14 and 1 and 10 to each other

8. What do these Tarot Keys reveal about the agent of testing?

9. What is the purpose of the work in this path?

10. Who or what is the subject of the operation of Tarot Key 14?

11. How does the fulfillment of our desires relate to the development of our character?

12. What does the direction of the flow of the current in this path reveal about the nature of testing?

13. How does a sense of the presence of the Holy Guardian Angel, shown in Tarot Key 14, affect attitudes toward the outer circumstances of life?

14. How is the element of fire related to this view of the Cube of Space?

Reflections:

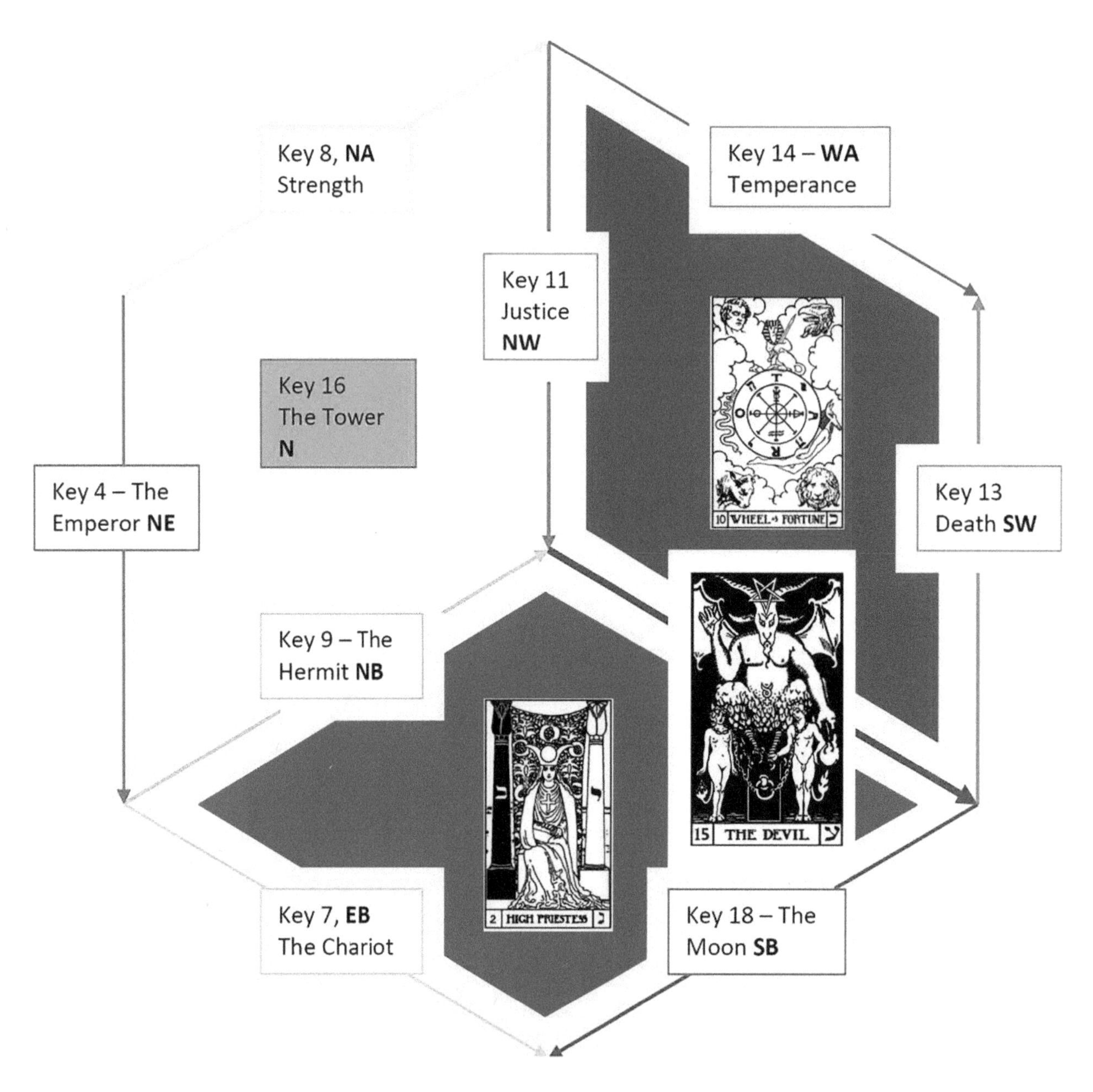


**Fig. 21**

West-Below Edge: The Devil—Capricorn

## Facing Reality

The line of West-Below is concerned with our current reality and how we are conditioned by our circumstances. The current travels from north to south. The attempt to separate external conditions from inner realities leads to the state of bondage depicted by The Devil. The predominant patterns we hold in subconsciousness (Key 2) work themselves out in the cycles of our lives (Key 10). This process allows us to see these patterns in manifestation (Key 15) and free ourselves from error. Meditate on this view of the Cube of Space to facilitate seeing through appearances and finding humor in outer circumstances.

### Questions for contemplation:

1. What do the Tarot Keys associated with this view of the Cube of Space reveal about the nature of human bondage?

2. What are your associations with The Devil?

   A. High Priestess
   B. Wheel of Fortune

3. What are the attributions associated with the Hebrew letter Ayin?

   A. Gimel
   B. Kaph

4. What are the astrological associations with Tarot Key 15?

   A. Key 2
   B. Key 10

5. How does Tarot Key 15 relate to Key 2?

6. Key 15 to Key 10

7. Keys 15 and 2 and 10 to each other

8. What in these Tarot Keys suggests the way to liberation?

9. What is important about working with physical conditions?

10. What does the flow of current from north to south reveal about the processes of embodiment and liberation?

11. What do these Tarot Keys suggest about the reality behind appearances?

12. How do these Tarot Keys relate to the symbolism of the Christ?

13. What is the source of renewal in this aspect of the Cube of Space?

14. Why are fear and ignorance associated with these symbols?

Reflections:

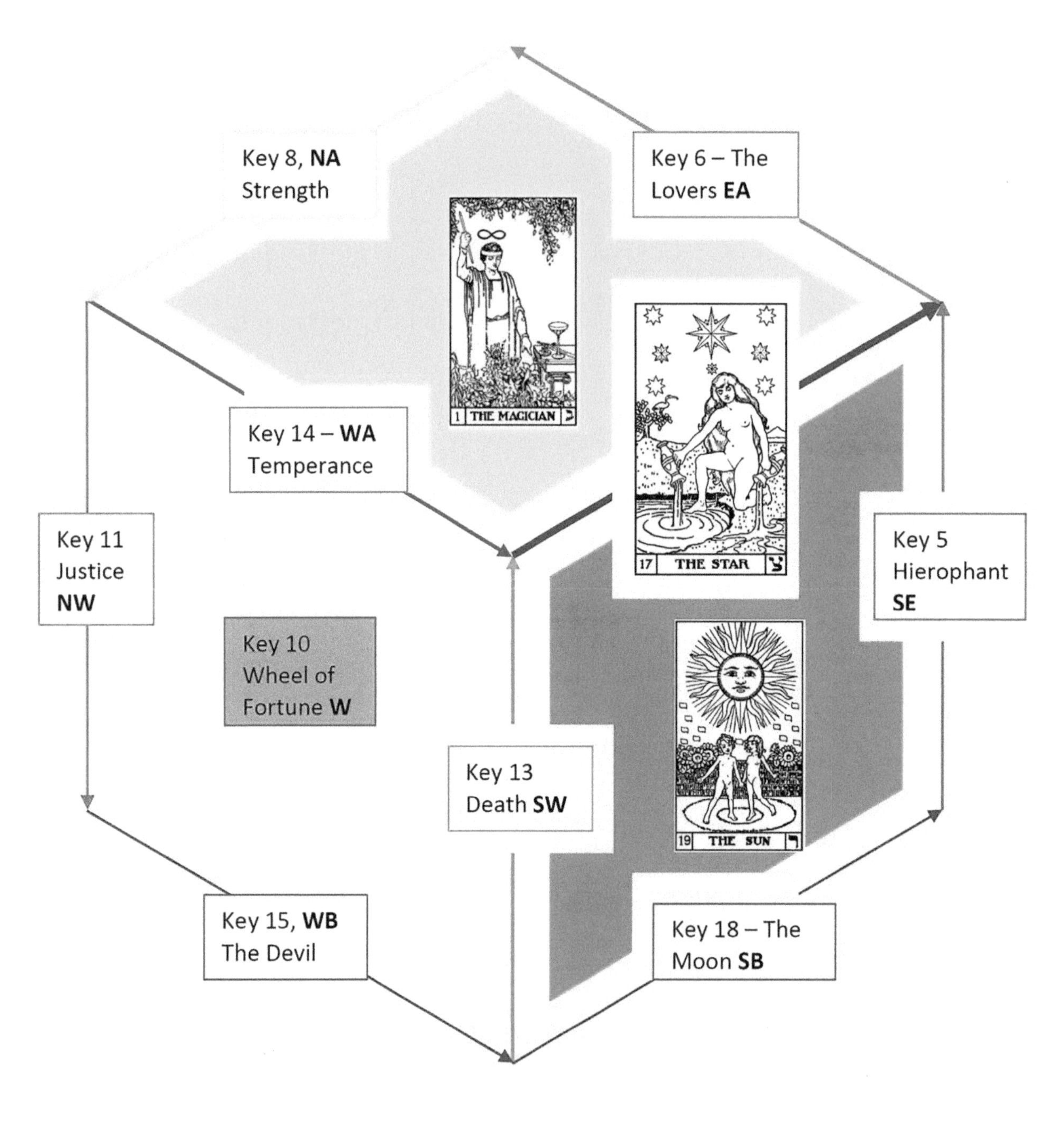


**Fig 22**

South-Above Edge: The Star—Aquarius

## The Truth Is Revealed

The line of South-Above symbolizes the revelation that results from meditation on the changing conditions of life. The current in this line moves from west to east. When we become still, centered, and receptive, we are no longer identified with the swirl of outer life. We begin to discern the point of view and purpose of the soul behind the circumstances of our personal lives. Meditation (Key 17) makes us more and more aware (Key 1) of the divine consciousness at the center of our life (Key 19). Use this view of the Cube of Space to enhance the effectiveness of meditation.

### Questions for contemplation:

1. What relevance does the analogy of fishing have to do with the process of meditation?

2. What associations do you have with The Star?

   A. The Sun
   B. The Magician

3. What are the correspondences to the Hebrew letter Tzaddi?

   A. Resh
   B. Beth

4. What are the astrological attributions to Tarot Key 17?

   A. Key 19
   B. Key 1

5. How does Tarot Key 17 relate to Key 19?

6. Tarot Key 17 to Key 1

7. Keys 17 and 19 and 1 to each other

8. What are the sources of light in these Tarot Keys?

9. What is the source of knowledge in these Tarot Keys?

10. How do attention and intention relate to this view of the Cube of Space?

11. How are stability and mastery suggested on this side of the Cube of Space?

12. How is liberation related to these Tarot Keys?

13. What does the direction of current in the South-Above line imply about understanding?

14. How does love relate to meditation?

15. How do these Tarot Keys relate to mental substance?

Reflections:

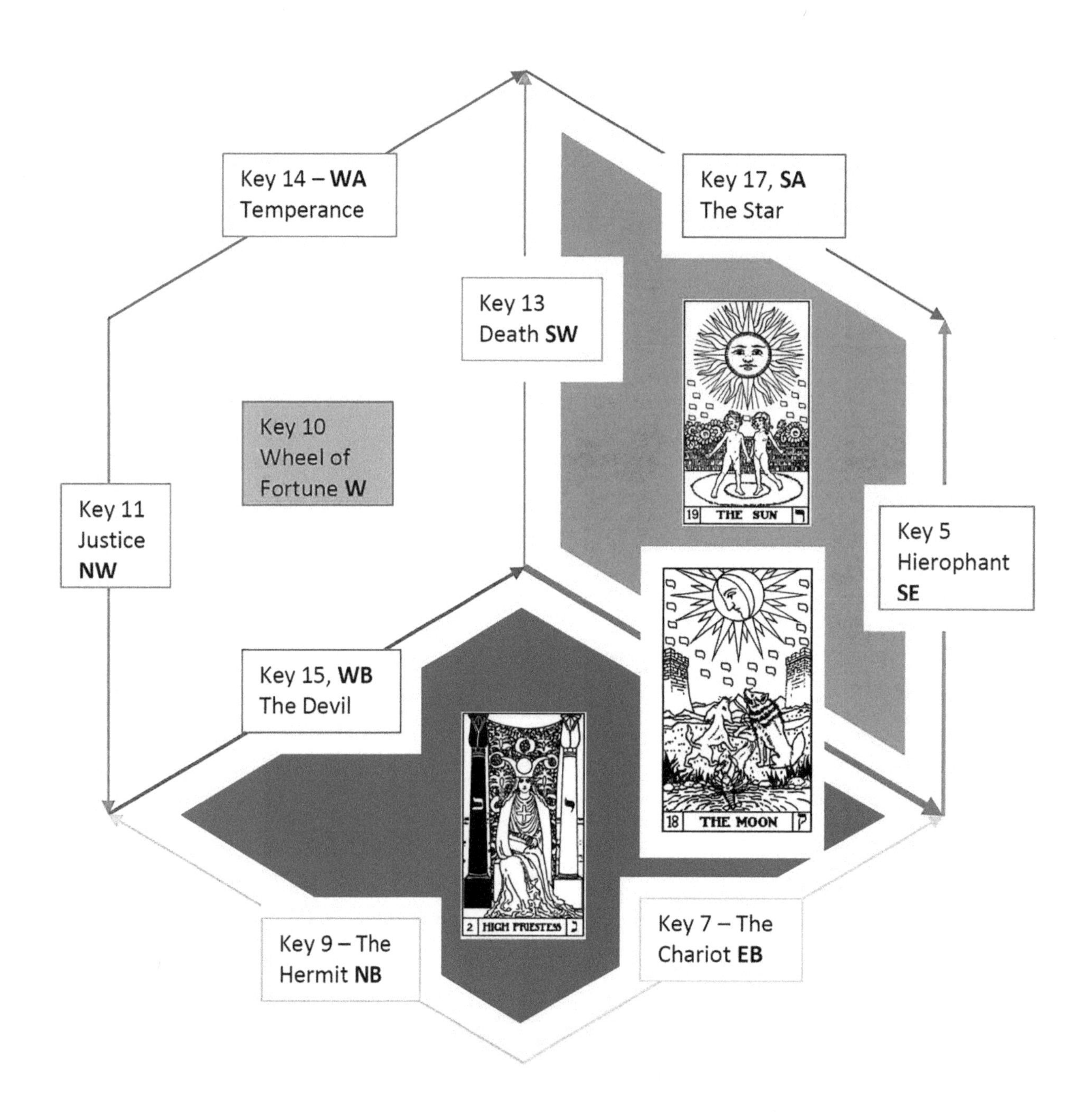


**Fig. 23**

South-Below Edge: The Moon—Pisces

## Integration

The line of South-Below concerns the reorganization of your body, mind, and circumstances as a result of the realization of greater truth. The current of this line flows from west to east.

As you walk the path of return, the habits of your mind and body become more and more in harmony with spiritual truth, until even sleep no longer separates your consciousness from the One. Light (Key 19) is incorporated into subconscious patterns (Key 2).

When realization is integrated into the cellular level of the body (Key 18), it is never forgotten. Meditate on this view of the Cube of Space to become more sensitive to the body as the vehicle of your service and realization. This path also shows the need to keep the perspective of the middle way as the safe and sure path to your goal.

### Questions for contemplation:

This is the last line on the exterior of the Cube of Space.

1. What does that fact, combined with the direction of its current, suggest about the process of integration, organization and the body?

2. What associations can you make with The Moon?

   A. The Sun
   B. High Priestess

3. What are the correspondences with Qoph?

   A. Resh
   B. Gimel

4. What are the astrological associations to Tarot Key 18?

   A. Tarot Key 19
   B. Key 2

5. How is Tarot Key 18 related to Key 19?

6. Key 18 to Key 2

7. Keys 18 and 19 and 2 to each other

8. How does the symbolism of these Tarot Keys relate to the path of return?

9. Examine the meaning of the element of water in these Tarot Keys.

10. What is the focus of consciousness in each of these Tarot Keys and how are they related?

11. What are the principles that determine right organization and how are they pictured in these Tarot Keys?

12. Sometimes when a person is struggling with a problem they are told to "sleep on it." How does this expression relate to this line on the Cube of Space? (Look at the lines flowing into and out of this line.)

Reflections:

# THE CORNERS

WHERE ALL THE INFLUENCES MEET
AND DIRECTIONS CHANGE

## Points of View — Getting the Total Picture — Going with the Flow

This section provides a more holistic view of the Cube of Space with an emphasis on the current of flow around the Cube. Having looked at each Tarot Key separately, the focus here is on how they fit together. This view not only helps integrate the Cube of Space for the student, but it also brings an appreciation of the Cube of Space as a symbol for the cycles of life. This expanded perspective gives us increasing opportunities for realization.

It will be assumed that the person studying this section has a basic understanding of the Tarot and the function of each portion of the Cube of Space, so comments will be general and will point out aspects of the relationships between adjoining edges and faces on the Cube. Combining this section with the earlier views of the Cube of Space related to the same Tarot Keys could benefit the student who wants to deepen his understanding of the Cube of Space and Tarot.

In the earlier section of the book, when the Tree of Life was referenced, the link to https://www.bota.org/resources/ was provided so that the reader could refer to the particular view of the Tree of Life referred to in these pages. To avoid too much repetition, I will not include that link with each reference in the later parts of the book. However, please use this link if you do not have your own copy of the Tree of Life.

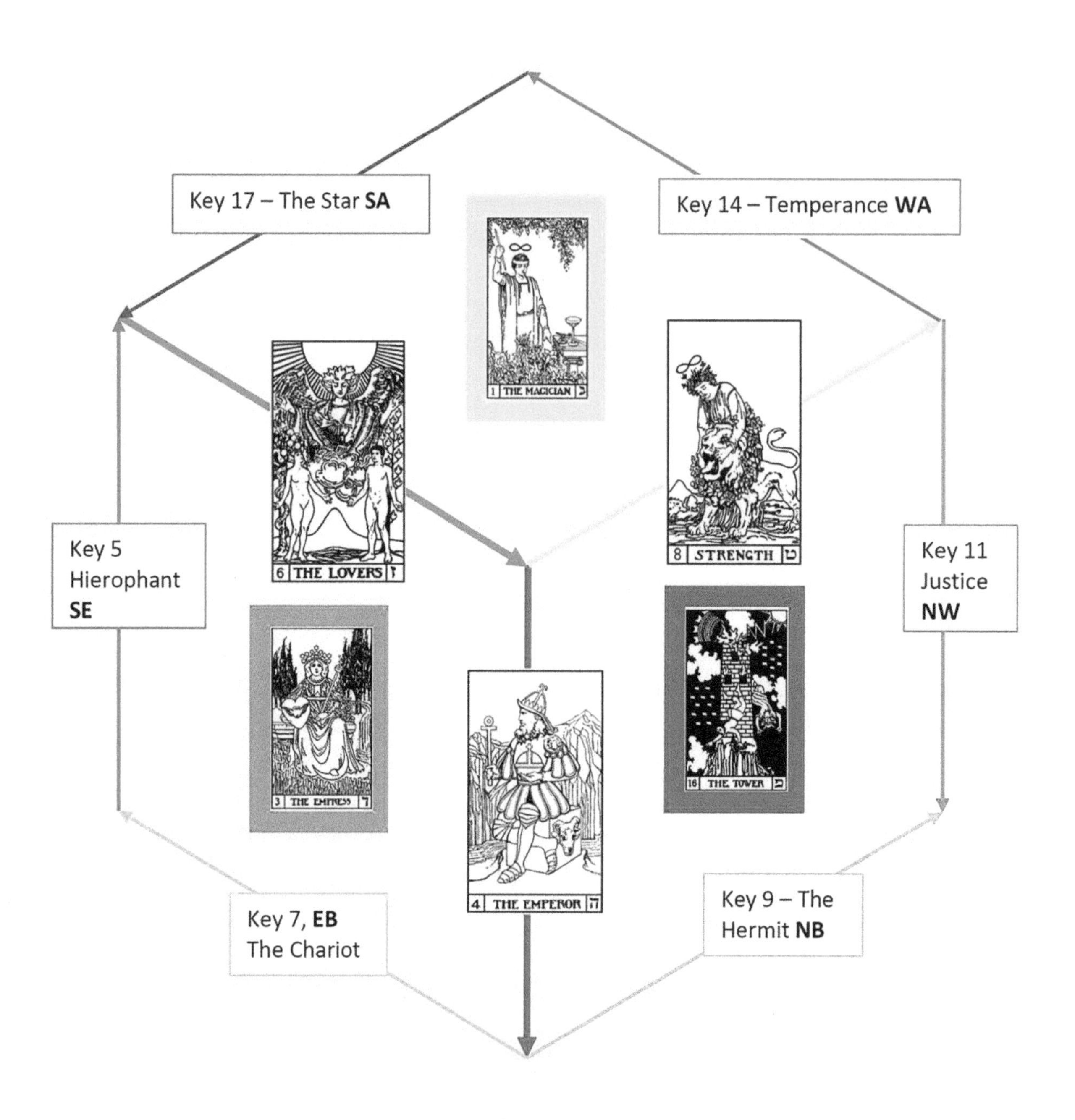


**Fig 24**

North-East-Above Corner

## The Starting Point

A new cycle starts with the impulse of desire. When a cycle has been completed, new possibilities are seen (Key 6) and with discrimination we choose a new direction (Key 4) for our efforts (Key 8). At this point we turn our minds (Key 4) and hearts (Key 8) in a new direction. The flow of energy enters North-East-Above from East-Above, bringing the seeds of the new possibilities out of past experience.

Through the path of North-East, a new vision is established by reason. In the path of North-Above the work of love, which realizes the vision in action, is begun. At this point we become aware (Key 1) of a new desire for creation (Key 3) which will awaken us to the required action (Key 16). Meditate on this view of the Cube of Space to become fully conscious of your intentions when you begin a new cycle of activity.

### Questions for contemplation:

1. Note the air of Gemini feeding the fires of Aries and Leo. What is suggested by this relationship?

2. Note the relationship of ego to desire. What is the function of the ego in a new creative impulse?

3. What color correspondences do you find in these Tarot Keys and how do they relate to the relationships between the Keys?

4. Note the sexual symbols in the Tarot Keys. How does sexual energy relate to the beginning of a new cycle?

5. How is love expressed in each of these Tarot Keys?

6. How do the planets, represented by the faces that meet at this point, relate to the signs meeting at this corner? (Key 1, Mercury; Key 3, Venus; Key 16, Mars; Key 6, Gemini; Key 4, Aries; Key 8, Leo)

7. One of these signs is mutable, one is cardinal, and one is fixed. Which are they and what does this tell you about the starting point of any activity?

8. What are the proper uses of the intellect, creative imagination, and action at the beginning of a new cycle of realization?

9. What do these Tarot Keys show about how the patterns of our past influence the realization of our future?

10. What do these Tarot Keys reveal about how past patterns can be changed?

11. How does the quality of your awareness of self determine the nature of your choices?

Reflections:

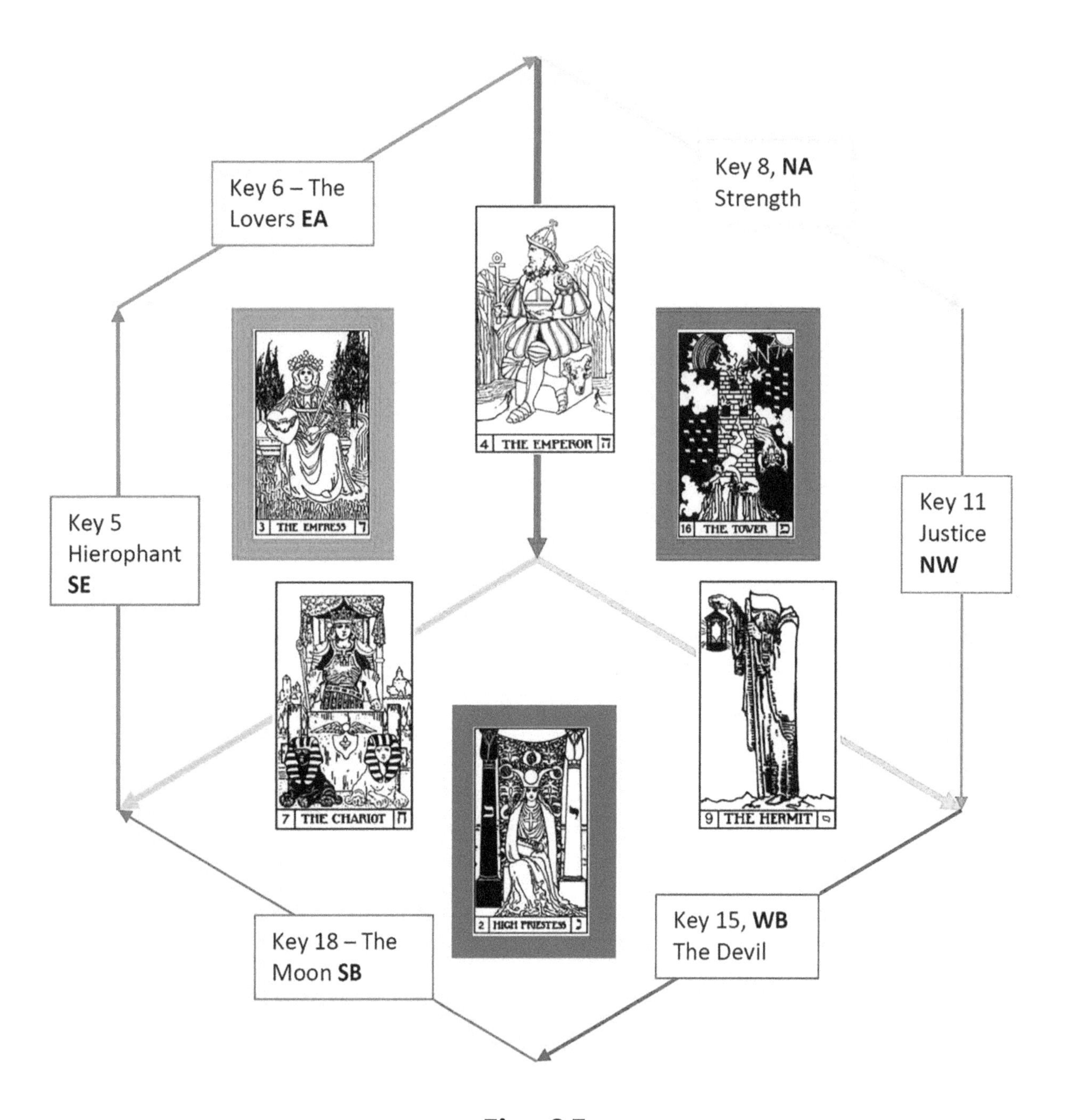


**Fig. 25**

North-East-Below Corner

## Point of View, Focused Will

Each new activity begins with an intention (Key 4), which expresses the will and vision of the actor. However, will is much more than conscious intention. This act of intention stimulates a subconscious process that makes us receptive (Key 7) to deeper levels of will power within our soul. A firm intention also triggers a response (Key 9) from the One, whether perceived as events in our experience or awareness of the Spirit's direction.

This brings us the inner and outer capacity to sustain will-power toward the achievement of our intention. The flow of energy enters North-East-Below from the path of North-East where the vision has been identified, and it leaves this point through East-Below where the creative powers become receptive to the direction of will. It also leaves through North-Below where an active response to the plan takes place. At this point the substance and remembrance (Key 2) needed to manifest the creative idea (Key 3) become available for our work and awakening (Key 16). Meditate on this point of the Cube of Space to intensify the will-power necessary for effective action.

### Questions for contemplation:

1. Note that the fire of Aries heats the water of Cancer and is contained within the earth of Virgo. What other astrological correspondences can be found within the influences at this point and what do they suggest? (Key 2, Moon; Key 3, Venus; Key 16, Mars; Key 4, Aries; Key 7, Cancer; Key 9, Virgo)

2. What does this point illustrate about the need for clarity of vision that comes from reason?

3. What does this point reveal about the relationship between receptivity and responsiveness?

4. How is will related to creation and destruction at this point?

5. What is the relationship between vision and will?

6. How is the quality of memory related to the expression of will?

7. How do boundaries function at this point?

8. What is shown about the subconscious response to intention in these Tarot Keys?

9. What is revealed in these Tarot Keys about the basis of our personal identity?

10. What is the function of the ego at this point and how does the quality of the ego impact the new cycle of expression begun here?

Reflections:

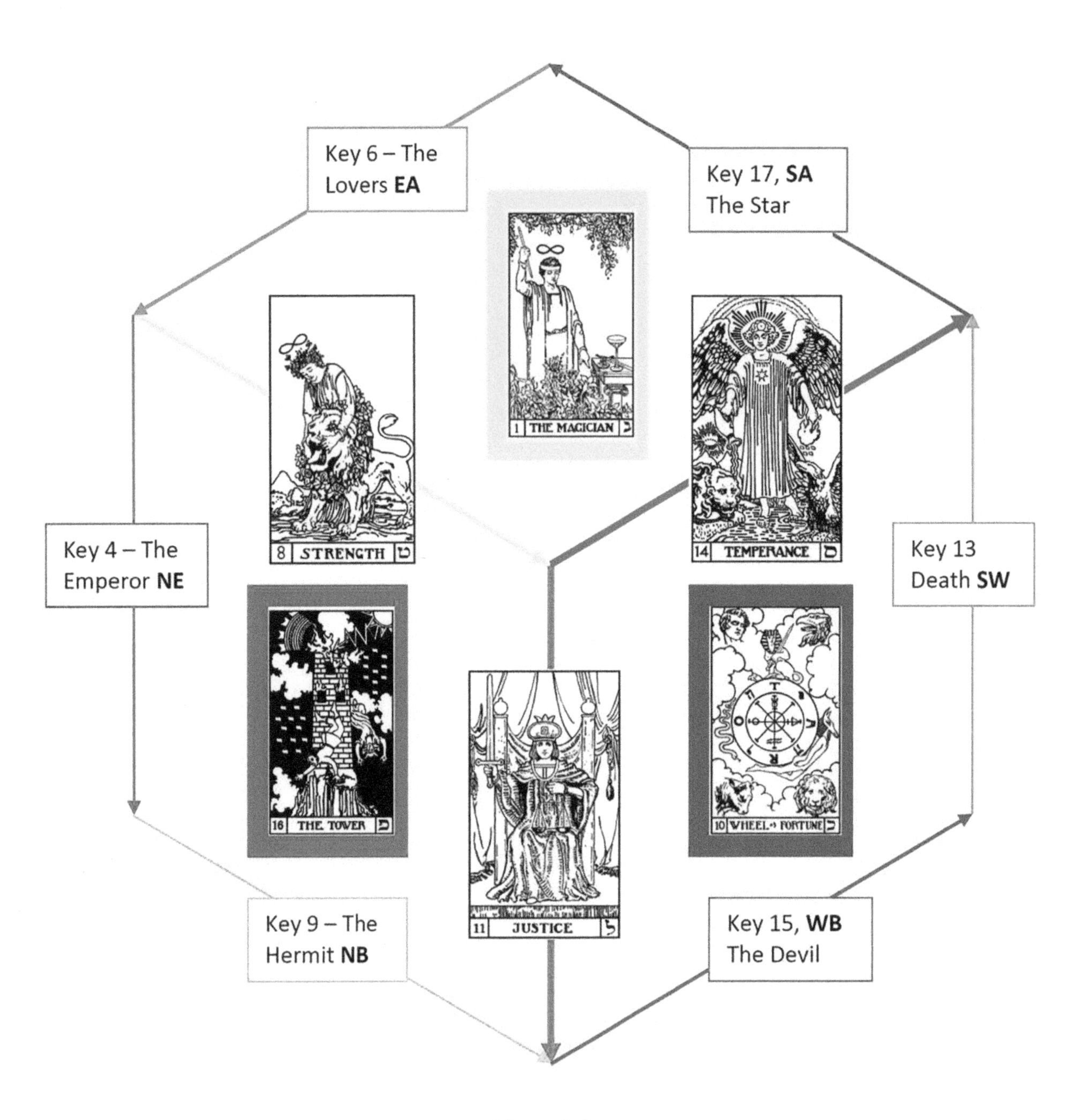


**Fig. 26**

North-West-Above Corner

## Point of Action

At this corner, the energy flows into the North-West-Above point from North-Above and leaves flowing downward into North-West and toward the South through West-Above. The results of the activity of suggestion (Key 8) must be balanced (Key 11) and tested (Key 14) by experience at this point. The desire must be adequate to sustain the work and struggle necessary at this point for manifestation to occur.

As we awaken (Key 16), we become present (Key 1) to our role as a channel for the divine plan which we can begin to see working in the cycles of our life (Key 10).

Meditate on this view of the Cube of Space to strengthen and sustain the capacity to follow through on the necessary actions to bring a vision into manifestation.

### Questions for contemplation:

1. How many types of action are shown in these Tarot Keys and what are they?

2. Who is acting and what is the motivation for the action?

3. What is the result of the action?

4. What is the importance of this point to the original impulse of the cycle?

5. What does this point illustrate about the value of work and the need for manifestation?

6. What does the actor become aware of at this point?

7. What are the color relationships between the Tarot Keys here?

8. What are the astrological relationships between the Tarot Keys? (Key 1, Mercury; Key 10, Jupiter; Key 16, Mars; Key 8, Leo; Key 11, Libra; Key 14, Sagittarius)

9. What are the positions and relationships between these Tarot Keys on the Tree of Life?

10. What does this point show about the relationship between action and reaction?

11. How is the serpent symbolized in these Tarot Keys and what are its meanings? (Look at Hebrew letters.)

12. How does the symbol of the serpent relate to action, work, and testing?

Reflections:

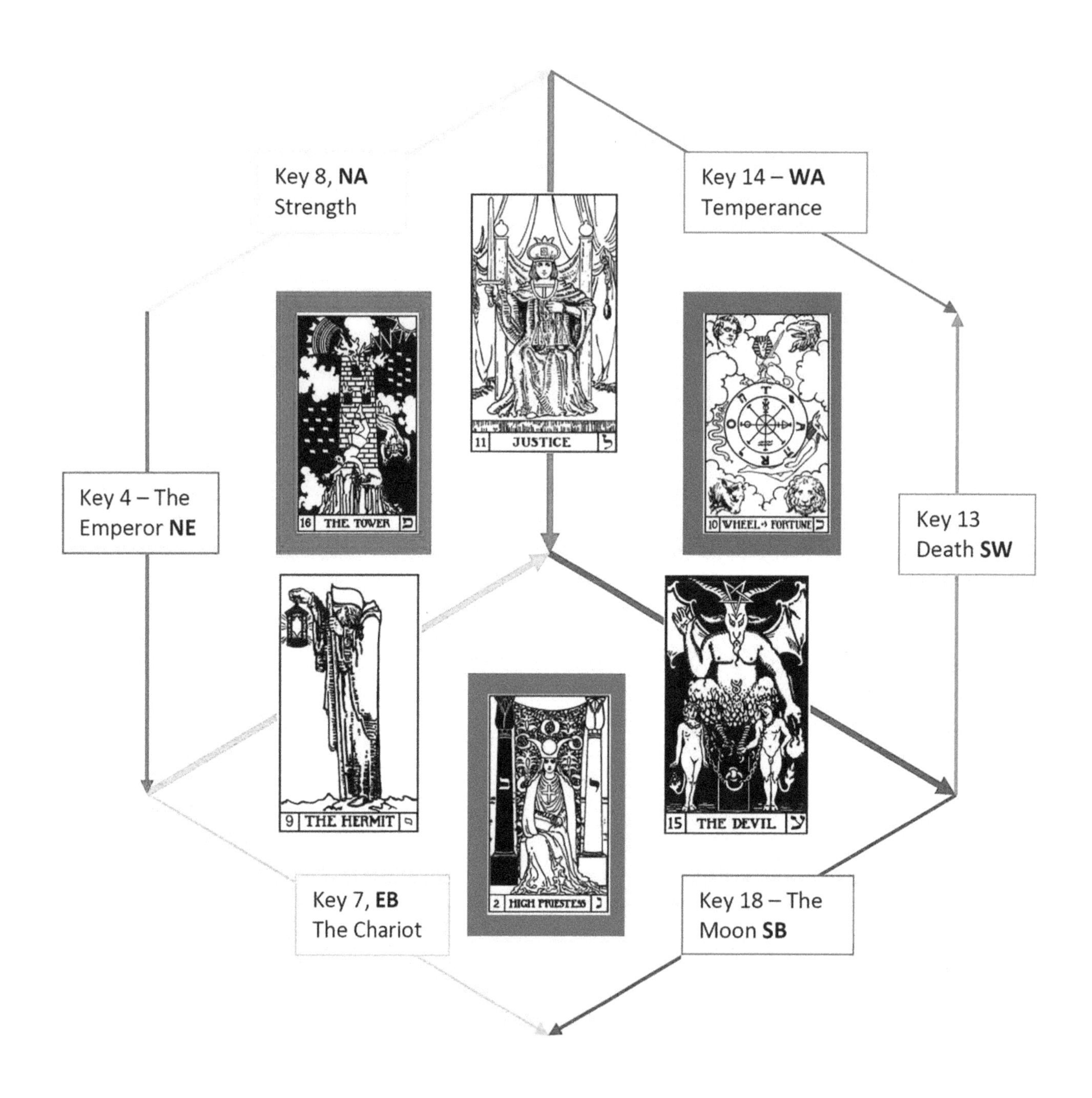


**Fig. 27**

North-West-Below Corner

## Point of Realization

At this point the form of the creative impulse becomes manifest. A new situation exists in time and space. In response to the will impulse directed by The Hermit, which has been brought into right relationship with the environment (Justice), the physical condition (The Devil) or (Key 15) appears. At North-West-Below the current of energy from North-West joins the current coming from North-Below to create the circumstance of West-Below.

Our actions begin to bring awakening (Key 16) as they interact with subconscious patterns (Key 2) to create the cycles of our life (Key 10).

Meditate on this view of the Cube of Space to become aware of the principle of cause and effect and how the circumstances of your life today are the inevitable culmination of all the actions and influences of your past.

### Questions for contemplations:

1. In what way could the astrological elements of these Tarot Keys relate to physical birth?

2. What other significant astrological relationships can you find between the Tarot Keys at this point? (Key 2, Moon; Key 16, Mars; Key 10, Jupiter; Key 9, Virgo; Key 11, Justice; Key 15, Capricorn)

3. What is the relationship between fulfillment, liberation, and bondage shown here?

4. What is revealed here about the purpose of limitation?

5. How do these paths relate to reality and illusion?

6. How does this point relate to our need for physical bodies?

7. What is suggested by the colors of these Tarot Keys?

8. Examine the relationships between these paths and those on the Tree of Life attributed to the same Tarot Keys.

9. What symbols of sexual energy are found at this point and what is their significance?

10. Why is The Devil surrounded by darkness and what has happened to the light that enters this point?

11. What is shown about the consequences of action at this point?

12. How is memory related to manifestation?

Reflections:

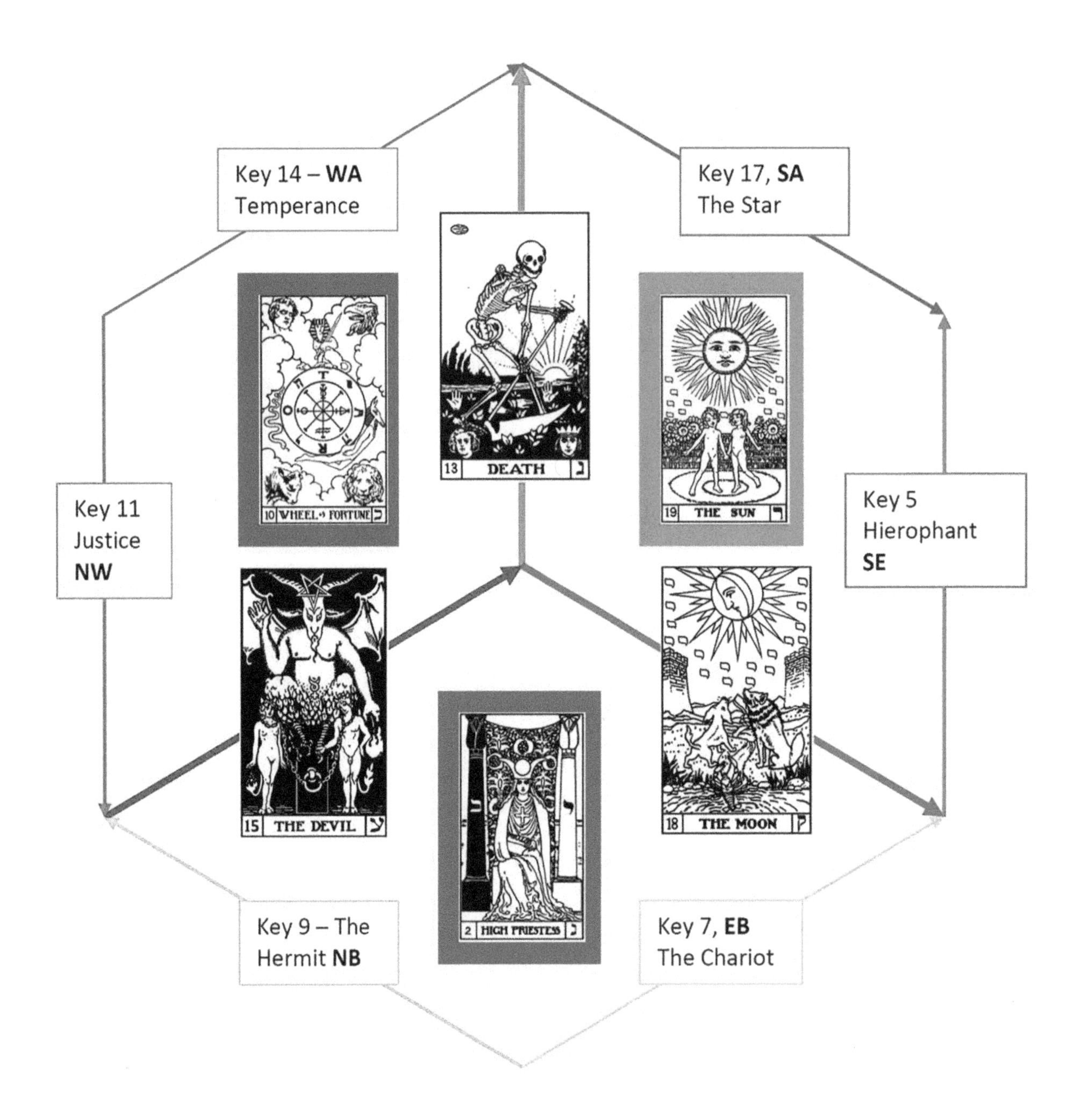


**Fig. 28**

South-West-Below Corner

## Crisis Point

At this point the manifestations of the initial creative impulse (Key 15) begin to break down as use brings wear and tear and the desire to modify conditions (Key 13). The adaptations and habits learned from experience are incorporated into the body (Key 18). As the forms that hold us break down, we progress along the path toward greater awareness. The current enters South-West-Below from West-Below and flows upward through South-West and eastward through South-Below.

When we remember (Key 2) that our personal fortune is a part of a much greater pattern (Key 10), then we can build our trust in the Love at the center of the universe (Key 19).

Meditate on this view of the Cube of Space to help release attachments to forms that are no longer helpful so that surrender to the deeper Reality can bring us greater fulfillment.

**Questions for contemplation:**

1. What do these Tarot Keys reveal about the purpose of change?

2. What are the astrological associations with these Tarot Keys?

3. What types of motion are related to these Tarot Keys?

4. What are the associations with reproduction in these Tarot Keys?

5. What becomes available to the aspirant at this point in the cycle?

6. What is changing at this point?

7. Why might one person experience fear and another liberation at this point?

8. How is the journey towards enlightenment indicated at this point?

9. What is the nature of the crisis at this point?

10. How are these Tarot Keys related on the Tree of Life?

11. What do the colors of these Tarot Keys reveal about their relationships?

12. How do these Tarot Keys relate to maturity?

13. How are Grace and Remembrance related to this point of crisis?

Reflections:

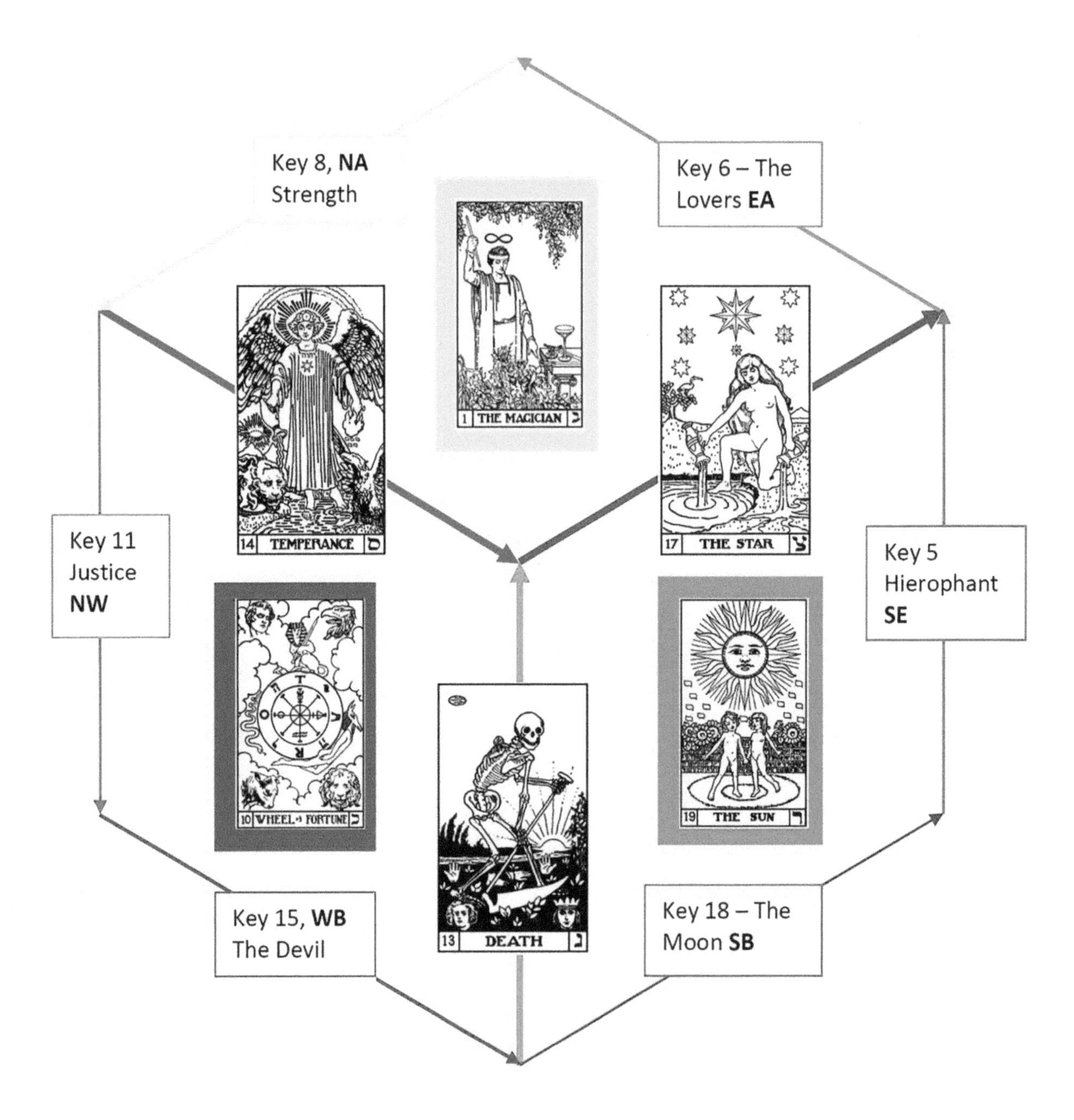


**Fig. 29**

South-West-Above Corner

## Point of Revelation

At the point of South-West-Above the process of testing (Key 14) and transformation (Key 13) combine to motivate the search for truth in meditation (Key 17). The purpose of form is realized in the West as the current rises toward self-conscious awareness in the South-West to join the current flowing toward the enlightenment of the South in West-Above.

The completed realization forms the basis for the revelation represented by the current of South-Above, flowing toward the East. Witnessing the cycles of cause and effect in our lives (Key 10) we understand our role as a self-aware channel for the life force (Key 1) which enables us to trust in the Divine Will (Key 19) behind all manifestation.

Meditate on this view of the Cube of Space to open the heart and mind to the spiritual meaning of experience.

### Questions for contemplation:

1. Who is directing the process that is taking place at this point?

2. Who is the knower?

3. How are these Tarot Keys related on the Tree of Life and does that add any significance to their Cube of Space positions?

4. How are the astrological elements represented at this point interacting? (Key 1, Mercury; Key 10, Jupiter; Key 19, Sun; Key 13, Scorpio; Key 14, Sagittarius; Key 17, Aquarius)

5. What are the sources of light in these Tarot Keys, and how are they related to the meaning of this point?

6. What does this point reveal about the impulse to meditate?

7. What types of motion are taking place in these Tarot Keys?

8. Is the process taking place here a natural process? Why or why not?

9. Is this experience universal in man? What forms might it take in persons who do not meditate?

10. Is death shown to be the end of a cycle of experience on the Cube of Space?

11. What is the relationship between North-East (Key 4, the Emperor) as the beginning of a cycle and South-West (Key 13, Death) as the end of a cycle?

12. What process begins at the South-West-Above corner?

Reflections:

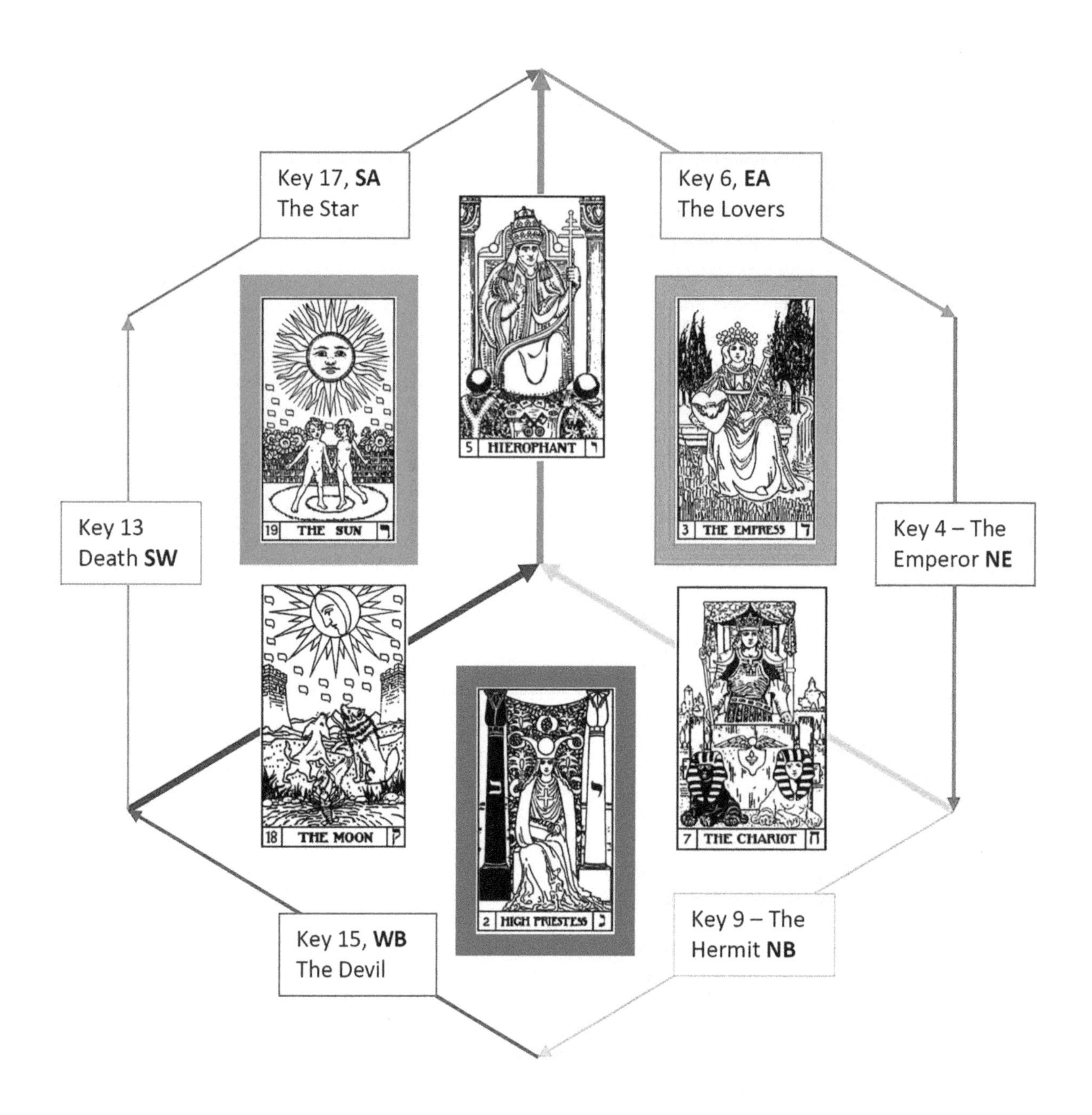


**Fig. 30**

South-East-Below Corner

## Point of Integration

At the South-East-Below point, the physical integration of the cycle of activity is being completed (Key 18). It joins with the field of creative mental activity, which remembers the original impulse of will-power (Key 7) to bring an intuitive understanding (Key 5) of the meaning of the completed cycle. The image of the water elements in the signs of South-Below (Pisces) and East-Below (Cancer) flowing together into the upward current of South-East brings to mind the idea of a fountain of life force behind the impulses of intuition.

The integration at this point unites (Key 2) all the levels of experience, intention (Key 19), and creative desire (Key 3) to formulate new patterns for our life.

Meditation on this view of the Cube of Space increases receptivity to the guidance of the inner teacher, which leads to true fulfillment.

### Questions for contemplation:

1. What are the correlations to the body in these paths?

2. What are the astrological relationships between these Tarot Keys? (Key 2, Moon; Key 3, Venus; Key 19, Sun; Key 18, Pisces; Key 7, Cancer; Key 5, Taurus)

3. What happens to the light at this point?

4. How do the positions of these Tarot Keys on the Tree of Life relate to integration?

5. How many symbols of receptivity are illustrated at this point?

6. How is the spiritual guide represented in these Tarot Keys?

7. What is the importance of love at this point and how is that illustrated?

8. Who directs the flow of water in these Tarot Keys? To what purpose?

9. What is shown to be necessary when traveling the path of life at this point?

10. How do the Hebrew letters associated with these paths relate to the concept of integration?

11. How many ways is the moon related to these Tarot Keys?

12. What is the role of memory to the activity of this point?

Reflections:

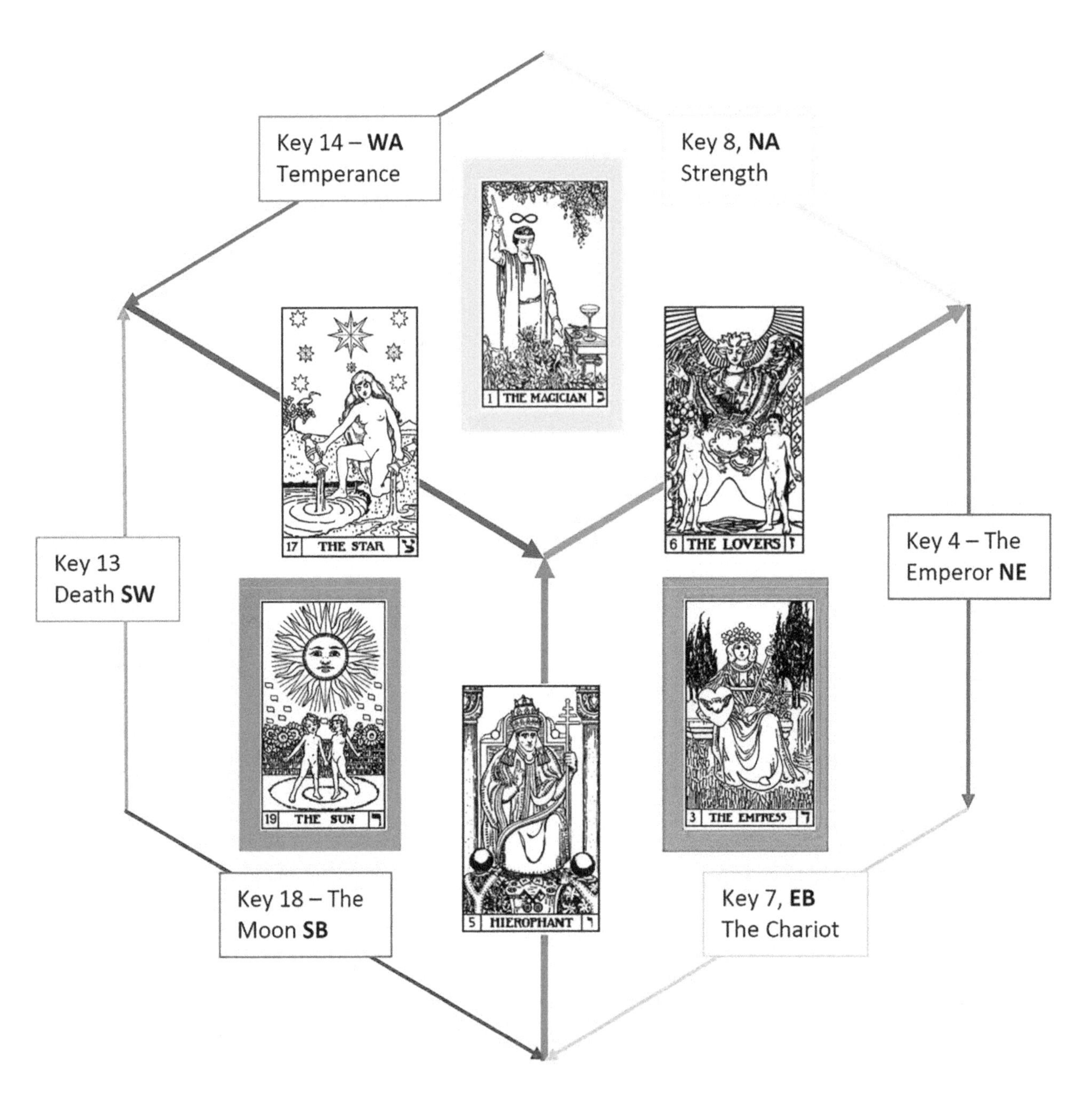


**Fig. 31**

South-East-Above Corner

## Turning Point

At the South-East-Above point, the revelation achieved in meditation (Key is confirmed by the intuitive Voice of the Inner Teacher (Key 5), which provides the discrimination (Key 6) necessary to move to the next cycle of expression with greater wisdom and healing. The meaning of experience realized in the South (Key 19) unites with the creative possibilities of the mind in the East (Key 3) to increase our capacity for self-conscious awareness (Above, Key 1).

With a deeper understanding of life's purpose and meaning, we are ready to formulate a new harmonious vision that will serve life more adequately.

Meditate on this view of the Cube of Space to distill the lessons of the past cycle of experience into the ingredients of a new vision that is in harmony with Divine Purpose.

### Questions for contemplation:

1. How are sound and vibration shown in these Tarot Keys?

2. How are sound and light related at this point?

3. How many ways do these Tarot Keys relate to communication?

4. How is communication related to making use of experience?

5. What is revealed about the nature of healing at this point?

6. How are wisdom and understanding realized in these Tarot Keys? Examine the Tree of Life for correspondences in this regard.

7. What are the astrological relationships between the Tarot Keys at this point? (Key 1, Mercury; Key 3, Venus; Key 19, Sun; Key 17, Aquarius; Key 5, Taurus; Key 6, Gemini)

8. In what way does this point represent a change of consciousness?

9. What is implied by the nudity in these Tarot Keys?

10. How are the proper relationships between the personality aspects of the self and the spiritual Self shown in these Keys?

11. How is love demonstrated at this point?

12. These comments have assumed an evolutionary process. What might prevent a positive turn of consciousness at this point?

Reflections:

# RETURNING TO THE CENTER OF THE CUBE OF SPACE

## THE DIAGONALS: THE FINAL HEBREW LETTERS

## Returning to the Center

We have been studying the exterior of the Cube of Space as a symbol of the reality of our lives. This symbol has much to teach us about our lives in this world and the meaning of our experience. However, as implied in the original study of the inner coordinates, our spiritual center is within the Cube of Space. In order to experience the divine reality at the core of our being, it is not enough to simply recognize the signs of God in manifestation and intuit the presence of something greater than our personality. To really know the spiritual essence of life, it is necessary to travel back to the center of the Cube of Space.

The paths to the center of the Cube of Space are symbolized by the diagonal paths which begin at the Below corners of the Cube of Space and travel through the center on the way to the Above corners. These diagonals are attributed to the final letters of the Hebrew alphabet, the five letters that have special forms and numerical values when they come at the end of a Hebrew word. Four of the letters represent the paths inward. The fifth letter represents the achievement of identification with cosmic consciousness at the center of the Cube of Space. This is the ultimate goal of our spiritual work.

The paths will be studied in alphabetical and numerical order. This results in Mem, which is attributed to the center of the Cube of Space, being the final studied after the path of Kaph. The logic of this order is that once any path is taken inward, the Center is experienced. To continue the diagonal outward once again is to reenter the outer world of experience. By returning to the exterior of the Cube, the opportunity for enlightened experience and service is available.

The opportunity to travel inward by another path is also available, each path taking us once again to the center and deepening our understanding. Once all the diagonals have been studied, return again to the study of Mem for a sense of the completion of the purpose of human experience.

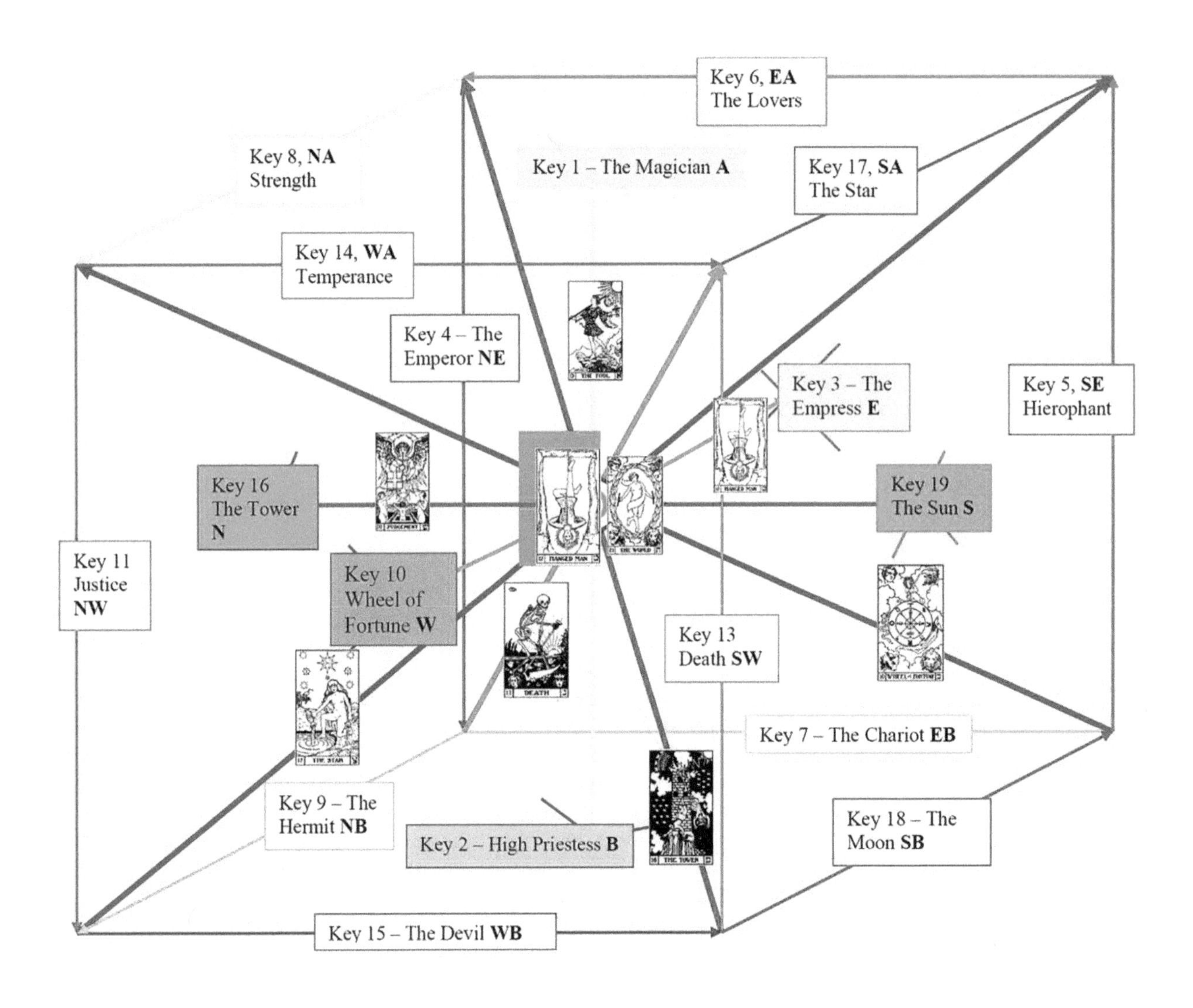


**Fig. 32**

The Interior of the Cube of Space with the Diagonals

## Going Within

The Diagonals on the Cube of Space are attributed to the final forms of the letters Kaph, Nun, Peh, and Tzaddi. As finals, they can only be entered fully after experiencing life represented by the paths on the exterior of the Cube of Space.

The fifth final letter in Hebrew, Final Mem, is attributed to the center of the Cube, along with Tav. The return to the center of the Cube of Space is the goal of experience, and it is symbolized by the Hebrew word *toom* (Tav-Mem), meaning perfection. At the center of the Cube of Space, one is in contact with all the interior coordinates. This is a place of perfect freedom, a state of cosmic consciousness and peace and identification with the source of creation. From this place one may choose to reenter the activity and consciousness of the created world, represented by edges of the Cube of Space, through any one of the four diagonals.

The form and structure of the Cube of Space may also be entered through the inner coordinates, leading to the faces of the Cube. One could therefore choose to bring the insight of cosmic consciousness into expression through modifying activity or form. The existence of the diagonals and the fact that they begin at the Below corners of the Cube of Space symbolize the inner drive to return to the source of our being. The fact that they continue to the Above corners of the Cube symbolizes the drive of Spirit to be known in manifestation.

Before each individual path is studied, it is helpful to examine the diagonals and the Cube of Space as a whole for patterns within the Cube of Space. The diagonals integrate the Cube of Space, as each diagonal intersects all the faces, half of the sides, two of the corners and the center of the Cube.

As you study the diagonals, a review of the previous section relating to the corners joined by each diagonal will deepen your understanding of the dynamics of each inward path. Since the diagonals integrate the entire Cube of Space, the Cube must be examined as a whole to fully understand the diagonals.

## Questions for contemplation:

1. How are the diagonals beginning on the North side of the Cube of Space related?

2. How are the diagonals beginning on the South side of the Cube of Space related?

3. How is the diagonal beginning at the NEB corner (Final Nun, Key 13), related to the diagonal beginning on the SWB corner (Final Peh, Key 16)?

4. How is the diagonal beginning at NWB (Final Tzaddi, Key 17) related to the diagonal beginning at SEB (Final Kaph, Key 10)?

5. How are the two letters at the center of the Cube of Space (Tav—Key 21) and Final Mem— Key 12) related?

6. What does the interior of the Cube reveal about the nature of liberation?

7. How are the diagonals related to the paths and faces where they terminate?

    - SEB-NWA (Final Kaph, Key 10) to W (Wheel of Fortune), A (The Magician), N (The Tower), NA (Strength), NW (Justice), WA (Temperance)
    - NEB-SWA (Final Nun, Key 13) to SA (The Star), WA (Temperance), SW (Death), A (The Magician), S (The Sun), W (Wheel of Fortune)
    - NWB-SEA (Final Tzaddi, Key 17) to S (The Sun), A (The Magician), E (The Empress), SA (The Star), SE (Hierophant), EA (The Lovers)
    - SWB-NEA (Final Peh, Key 16) to N (The Tower), E (The Empress), A (The Magician), NA (Strength), EA (The Lovers), NE (The Emperor)

- How are the final letters related to the inner coordinates of the Cube of Space? (Final Kaph associated with Key 10 (Wheel of Fortune), Final Mem with Key 12 (Hanged Man), Final Nun with Key 13 (Death), Final Peh with Key 16 (The Tower), & Final Tzaddi with Key 17 (The Star))

A-B (The Fool) related to Keys 10, 12, 13, 16, & 17

E-W (Hanged Man) related to Keys 10, 12, 13, 16, & 17

N-S (Judgement) related to Keys 10, 12, 13, 16, & 17

8. Two of the Tarot images associated with the diagonals appear destructive or traumatic and the other two appear constructive and balanced. How are these pairs related to each other and what does the position of these diagonals imply about the Path of Return?

9. How do each of the final letters lead to reversal and surrender? (Key 12)

10. How do the diagonals starting from the east side of the Cube of Space (Final Nun—Key 13 and Final Kaph—Key 10) relate to the creative impulse?

11. How do the diagonals beginning on the west side of the Cube of Space (Final Tzaddi—Key 17 and Final Peh—Key 16) relate to experience?

12. How do the diagonals beginning on the north side of the Cube of Space (Final Nun—Key 13 and Final Tzaddi—Key 17) relate to awakening?

13. How do the diagonals beginning on the south side of the Cube of Space (Final Peh—Key 16 and Final Kaph—Key 10) relate to enlightenment?

14. What does the fact that all the diagonals begin at the Below side (High Priestess, Key 2) of the Cube of Space suggest about the Path to inner understanding?

Reflections:

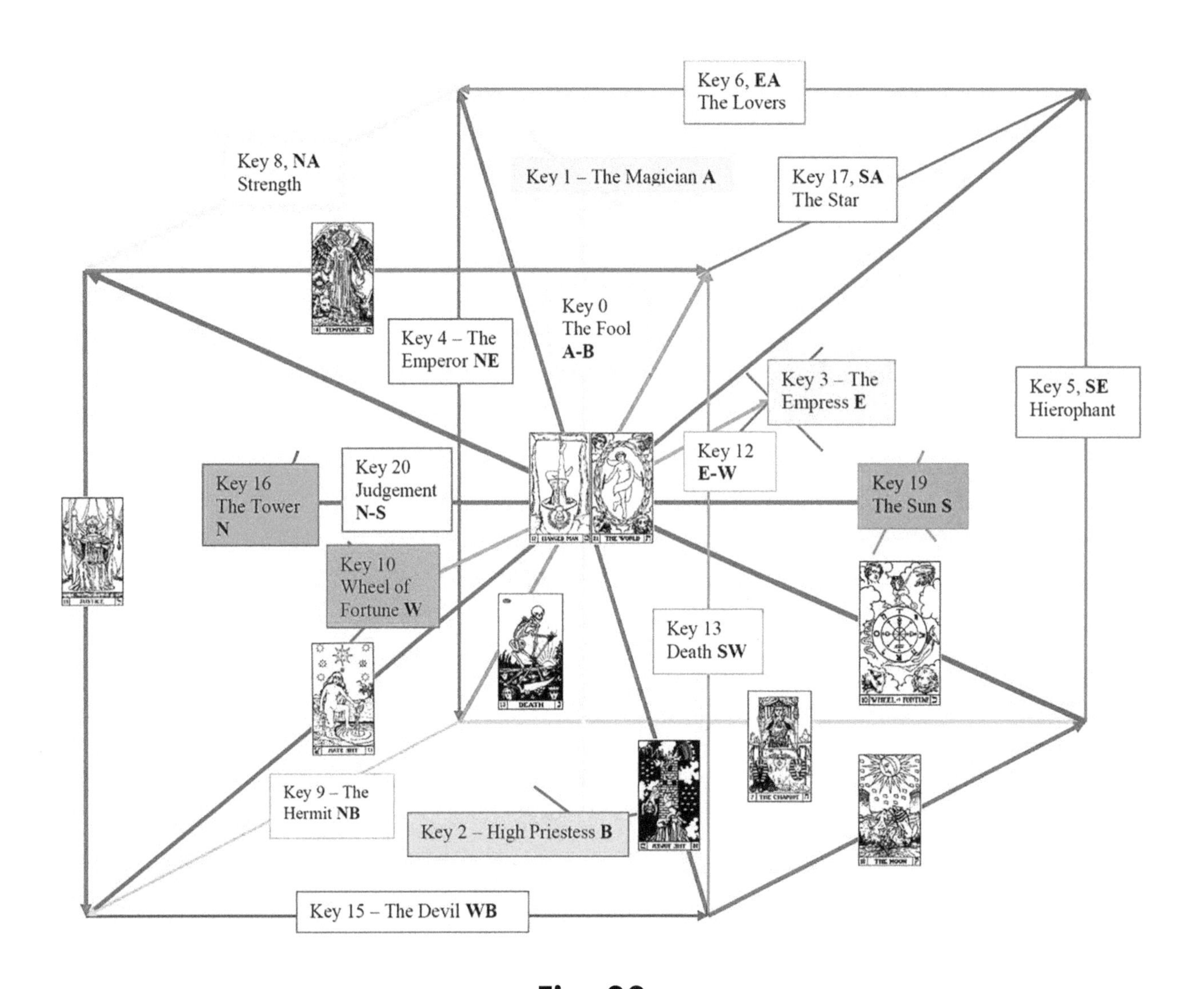


**Fig. 33**

South-East-Below to North-West-Above; Final Kaph

## Grasping the Central Reality

### Final Kaph — Wheel of Fortune

This is the first final in the alphabet. It begins at the South-East-Below corner where the energies of the South-Below line (Key 18) meet the flow of the current from East-Below (Key 7). This diagonal begins at what has been previously termed the Point of Integration. At this point, a profound expansion of consciousness (Key 10) is possible that takes us to the Center of our Being.

If this expansion of consciousness is carried to the outside of the Cube of Space to the North-West-Above corner, it impacts the action taking place and modifies the expression of karma (Key 11) as well as the conscious relationship with circumstances related to Key 14 on the Western face of the Cube.

Meditate on this view of the Cube to grasp the dynamic between the urge for expanded expression and the need for fulfillment that comes from uniting with the Central Reality at the core of life.

### Questions for contemplation:

Note the relationships between Tarot Key 10 (Wheel of Fortune) and Key 21 (The World).

1. What is the dominant element that flows into this path?

2. What are the relationships between The Chariot and The Moon?

3. How do Tarot Keys 7 (The Chariot), 18 (The Moon), and 10 (Wheel of Fortune) relate to submission and reversal?

4. How does the condition of the body relate to these paths? And what does this suggest for spiritual aspirants?

5. What are the relationships between Tarot Keys 11 (Justice) and 14 (Temperance) and Final Kaph (Wheel of Fortune)?

6. How are Tarot Keys 11 and 14 related to the Administrative Intelligence (Key 21, The World)?

7. What are the astrological relationships between this path and those that flow into and out of it? (Key 7, Cancer; Key 18, Pisces; Key 10, Jupiter; Key 12, Neptune; Key 21, Saturn; Key 11, Libra; Key 14, Sagittarius)

8. What would be the nature of the influence of this path on manifestation after passing through the center of the Cube of Space?

9. How does this diagonal relate to the relationship between form and consciousness?

10. How is cyclic motion illustrated in these Tarot Keys and what is its significance?

11. What is the importance of experience to this path and to the expansion of consciousness?

12. How are expansion and contraction related in this path?

Reflections:

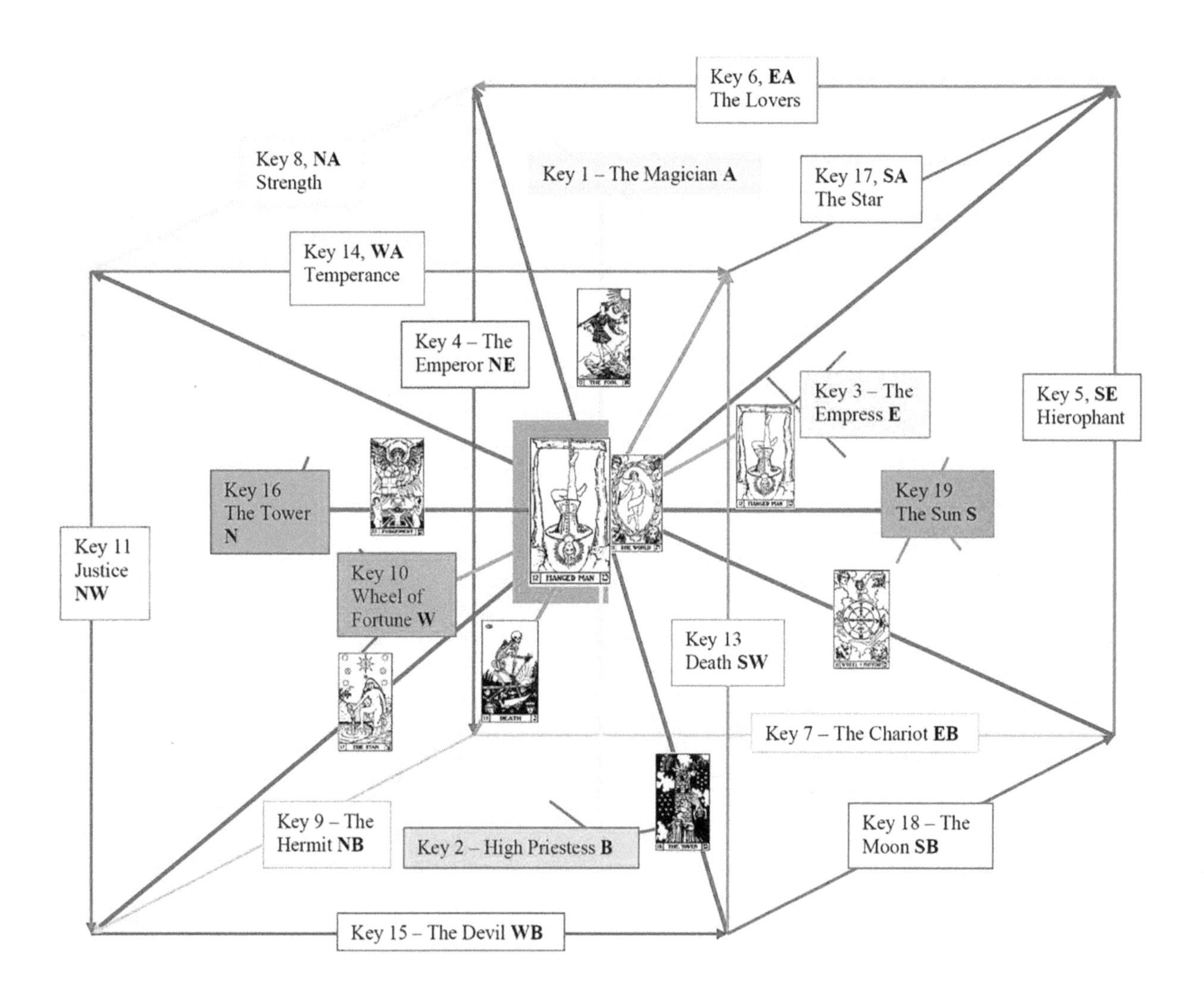


**Fig. 34**

Center: Final Mem

## Inner Peace

### Final Mem—Hanged Man

Final Mem (Hanged Man) is attributed to the center of the Cube of Space along with Tav (The World). Once we enter the Cube along the diagonal of Kaph, we are capable of the state of *samadi,* a deep meditative state of perfect rest in spiritual reality.

Our perspective is reversed as we experience subjective reality seen from the center of the Cube of Space, rather than the objective reality experienced on the exterior of the Cube. This is not the end of our journey, for complete understanding comes from taking the inner awareness of divine creative purpose back out into the objective world of creation as a servant of the divine plan.

The Hanged Man now chooses to serve from a universal level rather than from a personal perspective. Final Mem represents the state of consciousness realized at the center of the Cube. Joined with The World (Key 21) which holds the creative purpose, Final Mem represents the fulfilment of that purpose. Each diagonal passes through this point and incorporates this state of peace and unity.

As the center is approached from each diagonal, new levels of wisdom and understanding can be realized in enlightened being.

Meditate on this view of the Cube to become centered and fulfilled in perfect surrender to the Central Reality being expressed in all creation.

### Questions for contemplation:

1. What is suggested by the relationship of Mem as the East-West coordinate and Final Mem at the Center of the Cube of Space?

2. What is suggested by the colors of Tarot Key 12, especially in relationship to the inner coordinates of the Cube—Key 0, (The Fool), Key 12 (Hanged Man), and Key 20 (Judgement)?

3. Examine the astrological relationships of the paths that cross in the center of the Cube of Space Keys 0, (Uranus); Key 12, (Neptune); Key 20, (Pluto); Key 21, (Saturn); Key 10, (Jupiter); Key 13, (Scorpio); Key 16, (Mars); & Key 17, (Aquarius).

4. Examine the relationships between Tarot Key 12 (Hanged Man) and Key 21 (The World). How does reversal relate to the Administrative Intelligence?

5. Does Mem relate to the symbolism of baptism? If so, what does that suggest?

6. Having returned to the center of the Cube of Space and a state of perfect peace, why would anyone want to continue to travel back to the exterior of the Cube?

7. How is the idea of liberation suggested by the center of the Cube of Space?

8. The Hanged Man appears to be bound. How can this position be compatible with liberation?

9. What is suggested in this symbolism by the idea of the choice to travel along the inner coordinates (Tarot Keys 0, 12, and 20) or the diagonals (Final Kaph—Key 10, Nun—Key 13, Peh—Key 16, and Tzaddi—Key 17) to the exterior of the Cube of Space?

10. Traveling along an inner coordinate brings the traveler to a face of the Cube (related to a planet) while a diagonal returns the traveler to one

of the above corners and edges representing signs. What might that mean in terms of the symbolism of the Cube of Space and the Tree of Life? (Note the relationship between the faces of the Cube of Space and the Sephirah of the Tree of Life.)

11. What does the symbolism of Final Mem suggest about enlightenment?

12. How does the stillness of the Hanged Man relate his position at the center of the Cube of Space?

13. How might the fact that Final Mem and Tav are both attributed to the center of the Cube of Space relate to the inflow and outflow of energy at the center of the Cube?

14. What in the symbolism of Tarot Keys 21 (The World) and 12 (Hanged Man) indicate the nature of this energy flow? How is it related to light?

15. How are Tav and Mem related to perfection?

16. The center of the Cube of Space bisects both the Inner Coordinates and the diagonals and will be revisited as each diagonal is traversed. What does that suggest about the nature of the inmost reality?

Reflections:

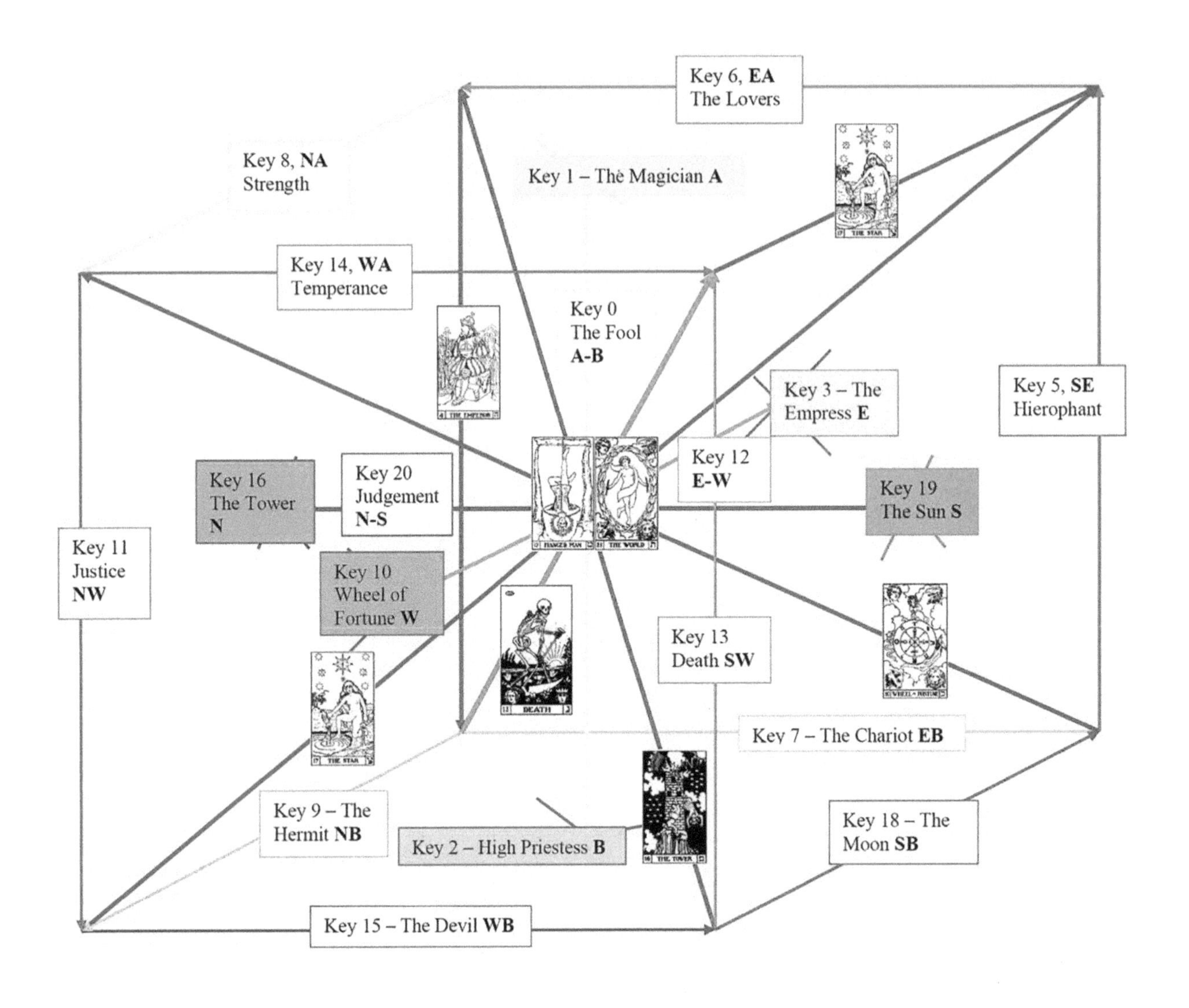


**Fig. 35**

North-East-Below to South-West-Above Final Nun

## Inner Transformation

### Final Nun—Death

Exiting the interior of the Cube of Space by any one of the diagonals brings you to the Above face of the Cube through which you experience Reality with self-conscious awareness. The paths downward are on the North side of the Cube. The first downward path is the North East corner, attributed to The Emperor. At this point a new cycle of manifestation is beginning.

The vision of The Emperor normally results in the expression of will-power in the outer world. However, when the reasoning process has been exhausted, a transformation of the self, represented by Final Nun (Death) can occur that brings us back to the source of our being. Old things will pass away and a new day will dawn as we come to understand the essential nature of our being. If this path is continued to the South-West-Above corner of the Cube of Space, where life's trials and losses have led us to the search for revelation, its power enters into the path of Tzaddi. Meditation on this path leads us to the growing expression of our enlightenment.

Meditate on this view of the Cube of Space to die into the transformation of our personal vision so we can experience the divine perspective.

### Questions for contemplation:

1. What are the astrological relationships between the Tarot Keys that flow into and out of this path? (The Emperor, Aries; Death, Scorpio; Hanged Man, Neptune; The World, Saturn; and The Star, Aquarius)

2. What relationships do the Hebrew letters and numbers on these Tarot Keys suggest? (Heh-4, Nun-13, Mem-12, Tav-21, Tzaddi-17) How does the ego relate to this path?

3. Does this path relate to physical death? If so, how?

4. Can you find any relationship between this path and the story of Jonah?

5. Where are the sun symbols in these Tarot Keys and what significance do they have?

6. Is this path about the work of an individual or the work of a group? Or can this path relate to both?

7. What is being reaped by the figure in Tarot Key 13 (Death) and what seed is being sown in relation to this path?

Reflections:

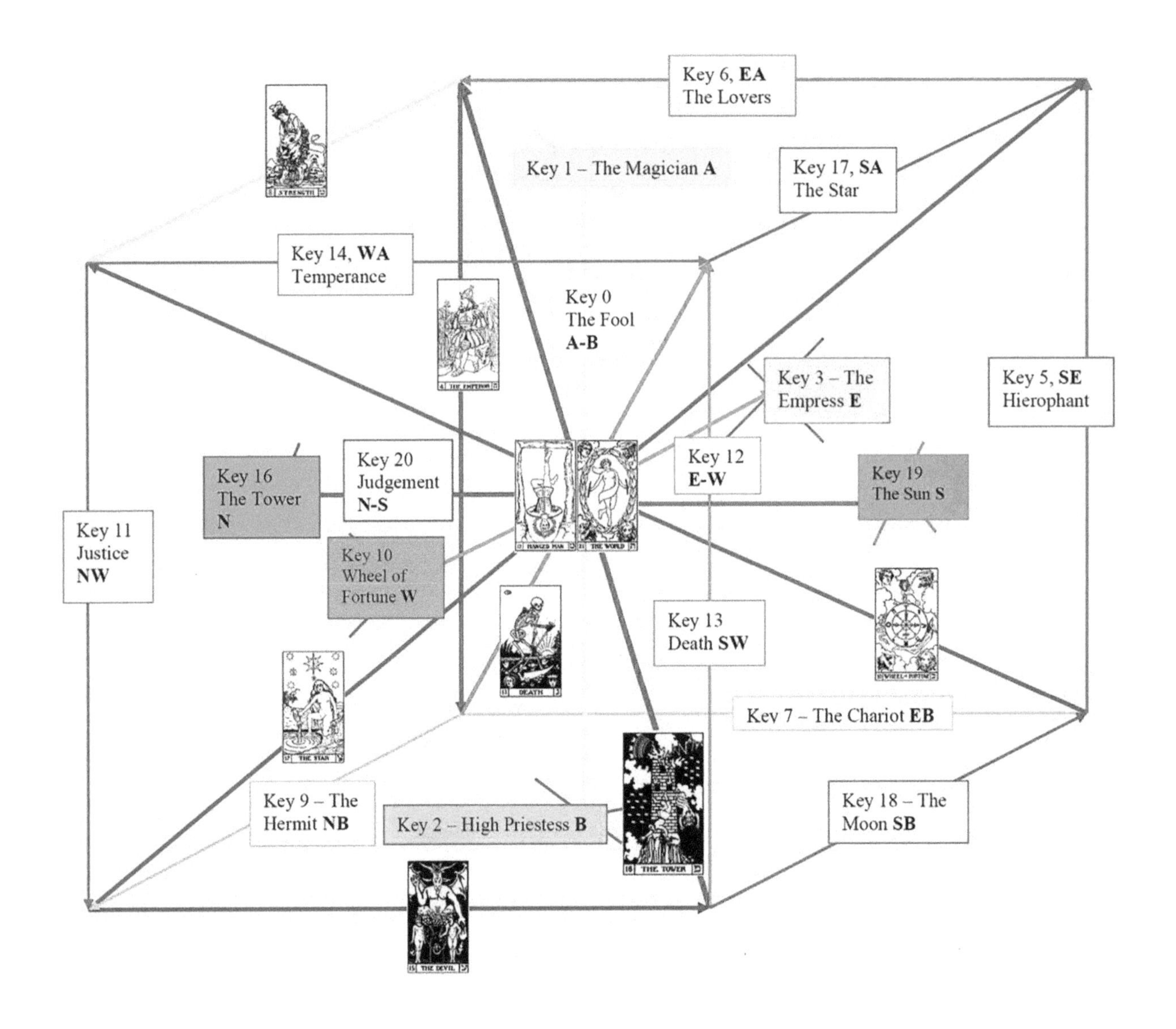


**Fig. 36**

South-West-Below to North-East-Above Final Peh

## The Grace of Inner Awakening

### Final Peh—The Tower

In order to traverse the next final (Peh), the Cube of experience must be traveled once again. In Final Peh, any identification with forms we have created, along with any bondage they represent, are destroyed in a flash of enlightenment. This awakens us from any remaining delusions and leads us to a new level of Self-Identification and the capacity for a new type of action.

Note that the South-West-Below and the North-East-Above corners of the Cube of Space that are connected by this diagonal represent the end and the beginning of outer expression within the symbolism of the Cube of Space.

Meditate on this view of the Cube in order to experience the enlightenment process as a manifestation of grace.

### Questions for contemplation:

1. What are the astrological relationships between the Tarot Keys connected with this path? (Keys 15, Capricorn; Key 16, Mars; Key 12, Neptune; Key 21, Saturn; Key 4, Aries and Key 8, Leo)

2. Examine the color correspondences in these Tarot Keys and note the relationships they suggest.

3. How does this path relate to the unknown?

4. What relationships can you find between this path and the preceding one of Final Nun?

5. How might this path relate to Geburah (Severity, 5th sphere) on the Tree of Life?

6. What indications of sound do you have in the symbolism associated with this path and how might that relate to liberation?

7. How is this stage of liberation related to the second column of the Tarot tableau? (The power of Key 2, the Moon operating through the agency of Key 9, The Hermit, to result in the process of awakening represented by Key 16, The Tower.)

8. What is the dominant element operating in this path and how does it relate to the paths leading to and from the work done in this stage?

Reflections:

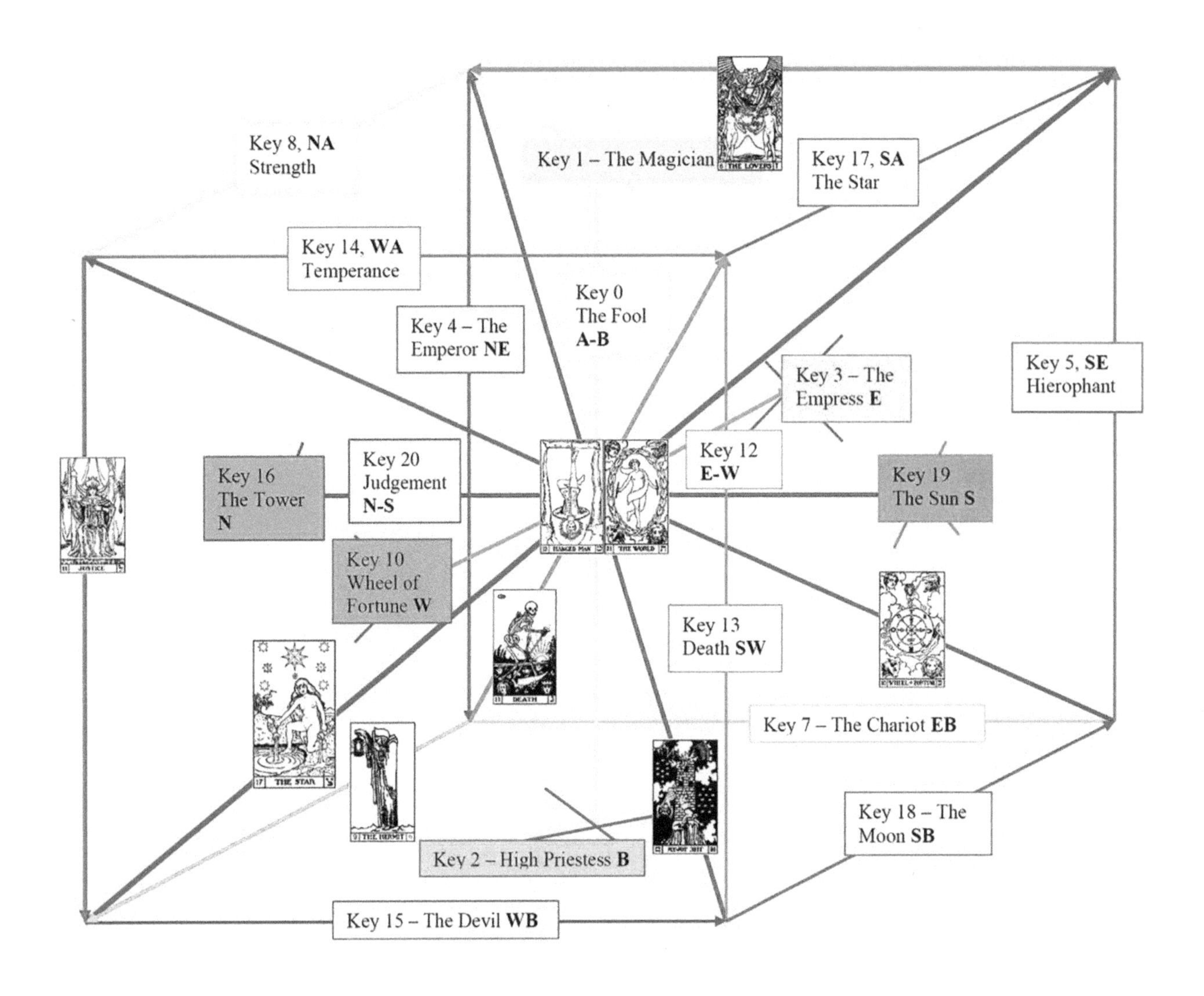


**Fig. 37**

North-West-Below to South-East-Above Final Tzaddi

## Inner Truth Revealed

### Final Tzaddi—The Star

When the unknown has been faced (North face) and the capacity for enlightened justice has been realized, the servant of Reality can enter into a state of deep meditation (Key 17), represented by Final Tzaddi. In deep meditation the soul can participate in the Cosmic Administration. The balanced, loving relationships between aspects of creation and between the Creator and creation are experienced. All the paths of the Cube of Space have been traversed.

The revelation of perfection at the Center of the Cube is sufficient to eliminate the necessity for continuing three-dimensional experience. The separate self has found fulfillment in unity. Yet the path continues once again to offer the opportunity to leave the union of the Center for the apparent diversity of external experience, offering continuing opportunities for love and healing service in the Kingdom of God.

Meditate on this view of the Cube to deepen the capacity for realization and enlightenment.

### Questions for contemplation:

Examine the astrological correspondences in the Tarot Keys associated with this path. (Keys 9, The Hermit, Virgo; 11, Justice, Libra; 17, The Star, Aquarius; 12, Hanged Man, Neptune; 21, The World, Saturn; 6, The Lovers, Gemini)

1. What are the relationships between the sources of light in the symbols of these Tarot Keys? (The Hermit, Justice, The Star, Hanged Man, The World, The Lovers)

2. What elements are represented in these Tarot Keys and what is implied by the relationships between these elements?

3. How are stability and fluidity suggested in this path (Final Tzaddi) and what does this combination imply?

4. What relationships between these Tarot Keys and Binah (Understanding, 3rd sphere) on the Tree of Life can you find?

5. What relationships can you find between this path and the first path inward, the path of Final Kaph?

6. What indications of perfection can you find in the Tarot Keys associated most closely with this path?

7. What is implied by the fact that this path begins at the end of the cycle of action represented by the North face of the Cube, but travels inward before the results of the action are experienced?

Reflections:

## Conclusion

If you look at the Cube of Space as a whole now, after studying it from each angle outlined in this workbook, you will see that you have acquired a meditation tool that will reward repeated revisiting. Those who use the Cube of Space repeatedly as they study the Tarot and Qabalah are rewarded with ever-greater insight. When you are studying a Tarot Key or a Hebrew letter, visualize its position on the Cube of Space to gain increased insight into its meaning. As a meditation tool, examine the issues of your life from the perspective of the cycles and relationships revealed in the Cube. Can you determine how your experience fits on the Cube of Space? What face or faces are you conscious of as you deal with life experience? How much of the reality of the Cube of Space can you be mindful of in each moment of your daily life? Try keeping a journal of how each day's life experience relates to the whole of reality represented by the Cube of Space.

My thoughts that have been hinted at by the questions challenging you in this workbook have just scratched the surface of the potential of this symbol. References to the Cube of Space in the writings of Dr. Paul Foster Case reveal the value he put on the study of this symbol. A fellow student, noted that the Cube of Space suggests squares of nine Tarot Keys for meditation. The central Key is the focus of the meditation.

A list of the squares is on the following page. Following that is an application of Cube of Space symbolism that developed out of a discussion of the process of social change. A reference page has been added with some of the attributions associated with the Tarot Keys. Also, two diagrams have been added that show the exterior of the Cube as a solid figure. Together, they show all the faces of the Cube of Space.

Each student brings to this symbol their unique background and readiness for insight. That capacity for insight also changes for each person as they travel along the path of life. Have fun with your meditations, both individually and as a group.

# Squares from the Cube

4 6 5
8 1 17
11 14 13

4 7 5
9 2 18
11 15 13

17 6 8
5 3 4
18 7 9

8 14 17
11 10 13
9 15 18

6 8 14
4 16 11
7 9 15

14 17 6
13 19 5
15 18 7

6 1 8
3 4 16
7 2 9

17 1 6
19 5 3
18 2 7

17 1 8
19 6 16
5 3 4

5 3 4
19 7 16
18 2 9

6 1 14
3 8 10
4 16 11

4 16 11
3 9 10
7 2 15

8 1 14
16 11 10
9 2 15

14 1 17
10 13 19
15 2 18

8 1 17
16 14 19
11 10 13

11 10 13
16 15 19
9 2 18

14 1 6
10 17 3
13 19 5

13 19 5
10 18 3
15 2 7

## Cube of Space applied to diagramming change processes

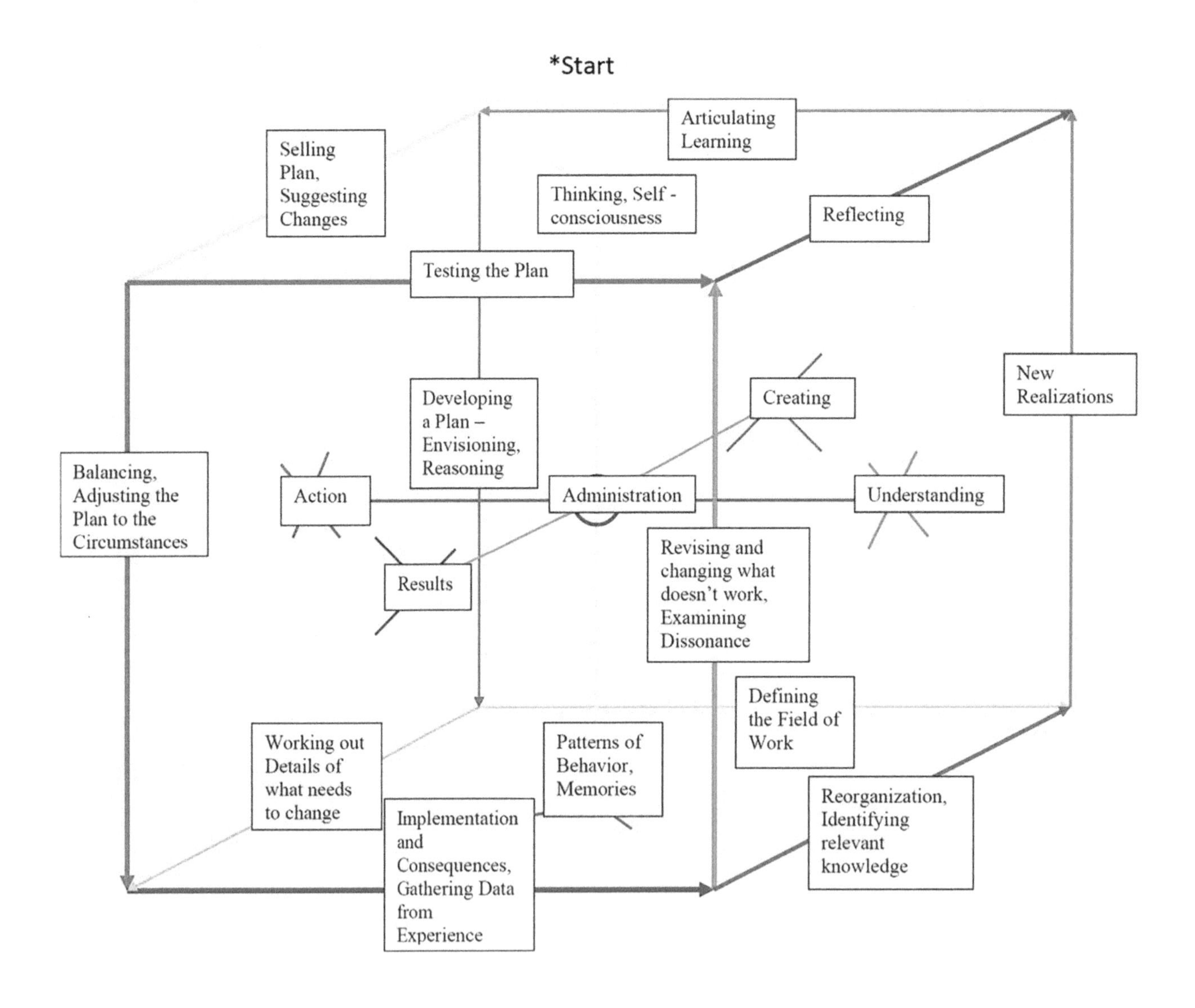

## Diagraming Social Change Using the Cube of Space

This is an example of using the Cube of Space to deepen understanding in a practical setting. Normally some of the factors involved in a group process to implement change are not taken into consideration, and therefore can potentially derail the process. The Cube of Space provides a structure that can map all the aspects involved in a cycle of activity. By referencing the Cube, a person can see all the factors involved. This could be potentially helpful in the planning stages of a project. It could also be helpful in diagnosing a problem that has come up during the process of implementation.

In a similar exercise, an individual can map a circumstance in life and see more clearly the levels involved in the experience. Through this lens, one can gain a better appreciation of the unity of life experience and all the factors involved in cause and effect.

When looking at this diagram the starting point is the top left corner and the line labeled "Developing a Plan—Envisioning, Reasoning." This correlates with "The Starting Point" and the line corresponding to Aries and Key 4. (See Fig. i and Fig. 1). May this study stimulate many new "starting points" in your life.

The next two figures show the Cube of Space as it would look as a solid structure. Together, they give you a complete view of the exterior of the Cube of Space

# North East Above

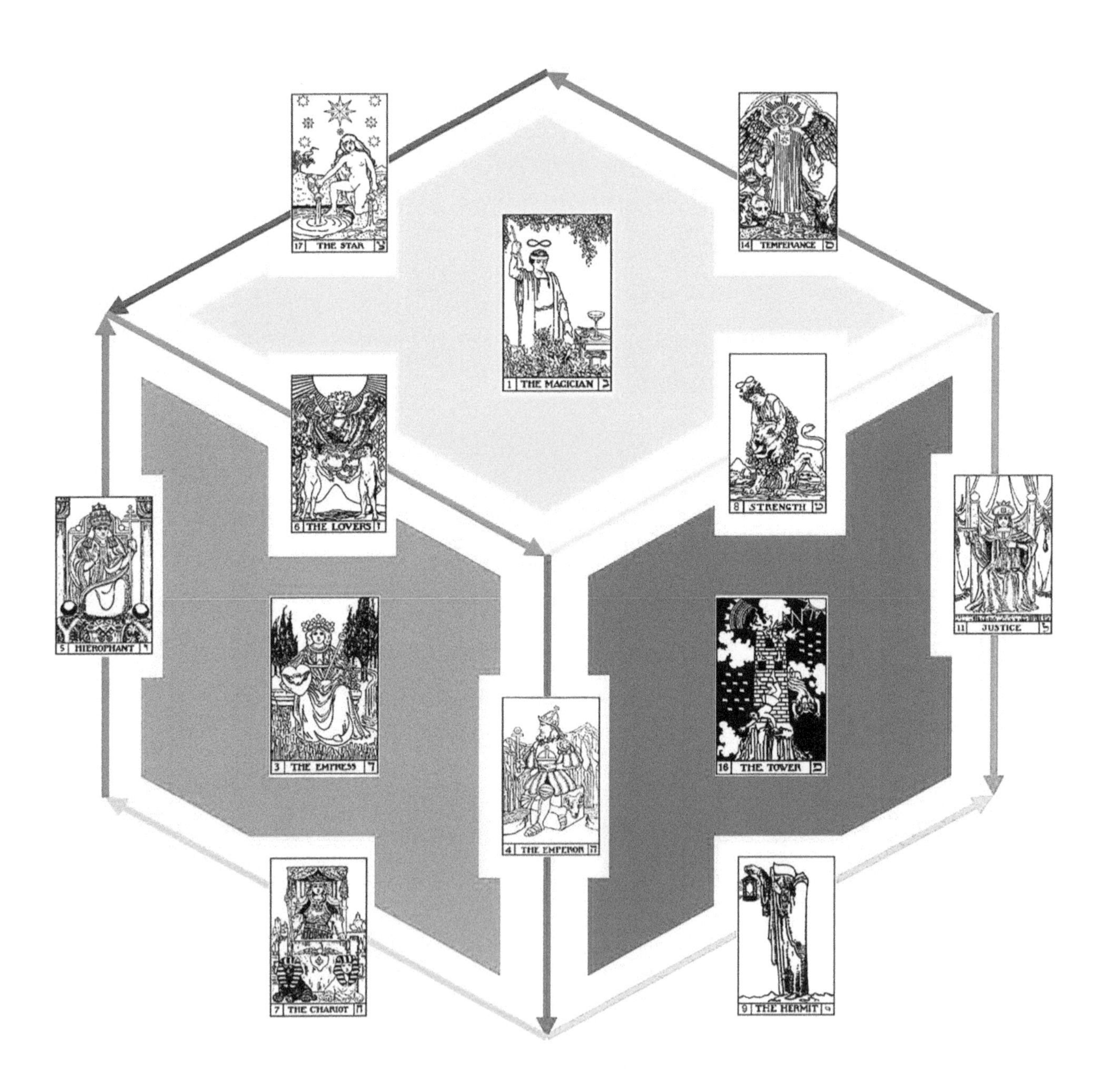

## South West Below

## Attributions of the Hebrew Letters and Related Tarot Keys

| Hebrew Letter | Key | Key Title | Astrological Attributions | Path on The Tree of Life |
|---|---|---|---|---|
| א—Aleph | 0 | The Fool | Uranus | between Kether (1) & Chokmah (2) |
| ב—Beth | 1 | The Magician | Mercury | between Kether (1) & Binah (3) |
| ג—Gimel | 2 | High Priestess | Moon | between Kether (1) & Tiphareth (6) |
| ד—Daleth | 3 | The Empress | Venus | between Chokmah (2) & Binah (3) |
| ה—Heh | 4 | The Emperor | Aries | between Chokmah (2) & Tiphareth (6) |
| ו—Vau | 5 | The Hierophant | Taurus | between Chokmah (2) & Chesed (4) |
| ז—Zain | 6 | The Lovers | Gemini | between Binah (3) & Tiphareth (6) |
| ח—Cheth | 7 | The Chariot | Cancer | between Binah (3) & Geburah (5) |
| ט—Teth | 8 | Strength | Leo | between Chesed (4) & Geburah (5) |

| י—Yod | 9 | The Hermit | Virgo | between Chesed (4) & Tiphareth (6) |
|---|---|---|---|---|
| כ—Kaph | 10 | Wheel of | Jupiter | between Chesed (4) & Netzach (7) |
| ל—Lamed | 11 | Fortune Justice | Libra | between Geburah (5) & Tiphareth (6) |
| מ—Mem | 12 | Hanged Man | Neptune | between Geburah (5) & Hod (8) |
| נ—Nun | 13 | Death | Scorpio | between Tiphareth (6) & Netzach (7) |
| ס—Samekh | 14 | Temperance | Sagittarius | between Tiphareth (6) & Yesod (9) |
| ע—Ayin | 15 | The Devil | Capricorn | between Tiphareth (6) & Hod (8) |
| פ—Peh | 16 | The Tower | Mars | between Netzach (7) & Hod (8) |
| צ—Tzaddi | 17 | The Star | Aquarius | between Netzach (7) & Yesod (9) |
| ק—Qoph | 18 | The Moon | Pisces | between Netzach (7) & Malkuth (10) |
| ר—Resh | 19 | The Sun | Sun | between Hod (8) & Yesod (9) |

| | | | | |
|---|---|---|---|---|
| **ש—Shin** | **20** | **Judgement** | **Pluto** | **between Hod (8) & Malkuth (10)** |
| **ת—Tau** | **21** | **The World** | **Saturn** | **between Yesod (9) & Malkuth (10)** |

Milton Keynes UK
Ingram Content Group UK Ltd.
UKHW050918190224
437940UK00009B/46